Dangerous Plants, Snakes,

Arthropods & Marine Life

Toxicity & Treatment

WITH SPECIAL REFERENCES TO THE STATE OF TEXAS

CONTRIBUTORS

TED T. HUANG, M.D.
Assistant Professor
Plastic Surgery Division
Department of Surgery
The University of Texas Medical Branch at Galveston
Galveston, Texas

S. R. LEWIS, M.D.
Chief
Plastic Surgery Division
Department of Surgery
The University of Texas Medical Branch at Galveston
Galveston, Texas

H. G. LOVE, JR., M.D.
Associate Professor
Plastic Surgery Division
Department of Surgery
Medical Director, Emergency Services
The University of Texas Medical Branch at Galveston
Galveston, Texas

BAKER STEPHEN LUCAS, III, B.S.
Herpetologist

DON W. MICKS, Sc.D.
Chairman
Department of Preventive Medicine & Community Health
The University of Texas Medical Branch at Galveston
Galveston, Texas

LINDA L. STEPHENS, M.S.
Research Associate
Marine Biomedical Institute
The University of Texas Medical Branch at Galveston
Galveston, Texas

Dangerous Plants, Snakes, Arthropods & Marine Life

Toxicity & Treatment

WITH SPECIAL REFERENCE TO THE STATE OF TEXAS

Edited By

MICHAEL D. ELLIS, M.S.

Associate Director
Poison Control Center
The University of Texas Medical Branch at Galveston
Galveston, Texas

DRUG INTELLIGENCE PUBLICATIONS, INC., HAMILTON, ILLINOIS 62341

PRINTED IN THE UNITED STATES OF AMERICA BY THE HAMILTON PRESS, INC., HAMILTON, ILLINOIS 62341

Development of this publication was supported by Grant Nos. 5G03 RM0000-04 and 5G03 RM00007-06 from the Regional Medical Programs Service. However, its contents are solely the responsibility of the Poison Control Center, the University of Texas Medical Branch and the Texas Regional Medical Program, Inc. and are in no way the responsibility of the Division of Medical Programs, the Health Resources Administration, or the Department of Health, Education, and Welfare.

DEDICATED TO THE MEMORY OF

CARL C. ALBERS

WHO WAS AN INSPIRATION `
TO ALL WHO KNEW HIM

TABLE OF CONTENTS

PREFACE

The United States contains a vast assemblage of plant and animal life. The flora and fauna are distributed in diverse ecosystems that range from the high mountain country to the community life of the coral reefs. Each of these environments contain plant and animal life that are potentially harmful to man.

The many and diverse animals and plants found throughout the United States make it quite likely that man will both frequently come into contact with dangerous organisms, and suffer the consequences of such an encounter. Emergency medical treatment must be given to numerous people with injuries received from any number of plants or animals.

The responsibility for giving the appropriate treatment for a large variety of bites, cuts, stings, envenomations, *et cetera,* falls on physicians, veterinarians and certain groups of paramedical personnel. Although a single volume containing a photographic and verbal description of dangerous plants and animals found in the United States is a necessity for these persons charged with the treatment of injuries resulting from the contact or ingestion of such organisms, no such reference currently exists. It is hoped that this compilation will help fill that need.

Symptoms and treatment are necessary features coupled with comments on prevention of injury. In the description of different plants and animals, it is vital that the reader have a sufficient amount of information so that an accurate identification of the offending plant or animal may be established.

This book was orginally published under the title *Dangerous Plants, Snakes, Arthropods and Marine Life of Texas.* However, since its content applies to a geographic area much larger than this single state, Drug Intelligence Publications, Inc. decided to reissue the book under its new, more general title.

ACKNOWLEDGEMENTS

We wish to thank the large number of individuals who have been of immeasurable assistance in the preparation of this text. We are indebted to the encouragement received from Dr. Truman G. Blocker, Jr. and the financial support of the manuscript by the Regional Medical Program of Texas.

The pictures of a large number of the plants included herein are a direct result of the invaluable help provided by the Soil Conservation Service, U.S. Dept. of Agriculture; and particularly Mr. Edward E. Thomas, Mr. Don Pendleton, and Mr. C. A. Rechenthin. We are particularly grateful to Mr. Marcus F. Wichman and Mr. Ray Blackwell, District Conservationists, S.C.S.; as well as Mr. Neville Smart, Jr. whose assistance in the field made the task of finding plant specimens much easier. We would also like to thank Dr. Rene R. Kempen for his encouragement and assistance to us in obtaining several plant pictures.

For allowing us to use their previously published material we would like to thank Frank W. Gould; Texas A&M University, Texas Agricultural Experiment Station; The Merck Co., Inc. (Rahway, N.J.); Dr. Julia Morton; Hurricane House Publishers, Inc. (Miami, Fla.); Dr. Cheston M. Berlin, Jr.; the American Academy of Pediatrics; John E. Werler; the Texas Parks & Wildlife Department; Dr. D. H. Davies; Dr. G. D. Campbell; and the *Journal of the Royal Naval Medical Service.* We are also thankful to Dr. Bruce W. Halstead, Dr. John E. Randall, and T.F.H. Publications, Inc. (Neptune City, N.J.) for their permission to use a considerable number of pictures as well as information from their publications. Our gradilude is also extended to the Crosman Seed Corporation (East Rochester, N.Y.) and the Northrup, King & Company (Minneapolis, Minn.) for their assistance in providing us with appropriate seed packages and for granting us permission to use them in the text.

We are most grateful to Mr. Kenneth A. Jones (Sea-Arama Marine World, Galveston, Tex.); Mr. Jonathon A. Campbell, Mr. Terry G. Hulsey, and Mr. Kerry Kellam (Ft. Worth Zoological Park, Ft. Worth, Tex.); Big Bend National Park (National Park Service); Mr. Bill Wardle (Texas A & M University, College of Marine Sciences & Maritime Resources); as well as Mr. Jim H. Whitcomb, Mr. J. M. Coffield, Dr. Paul N. Morgan, Mr. Roger J. Neubauer, Mrs. Carl C. Albers, Mr. John Otis, and Mr. Elkan J. Morris for their assistance in providing us with either pictures or specimens of the many species included in this text. We also wish to thank Dr. S. Harold Reuter, Mr. Denny Bowman, Mr. Hugh Vance, Dr. Charles E. Lane, Mr. Tim L. Turnbull, Dr. Richard Zingula, Mr. Antonio J. Campos, Mr. John D. Merritt, and Mr. Edmond S. Alexander for the contribution of superb photography, without which, the marine life section would not have been possible. We are indebted to Mrs. Laura Bauer and Mr. Gilbert Zamora of the National Marine Fisheries Service; and Mr. Robert Alderdice and Mr. Ken Yoakum of the Flower Garden Ocean Research Center, Marine Biomedical Institute (Galveston, Tex.) for their assistance in providing both marine specimens and photographs of marine life.

We also wish to thank Dr. James E. Blankenship of the Marine Biomedical Institute for the use of the aquaria facility for housing many of our specimens. We are grateful for the advice and guidance of Dr. William O. Willis and the advice and critical review of the manuscript by Dr. William Hulet of the Marine Biomedical Institute. We would also like to extend our thanks to Mr. Philip S. Flake, III and Mr. George Nations for their assistance in the selection of some of the dangerous marine species.

We would like to express our graditude to the Medical Illustration Service, the University of Texas Medical Branch at Galveston and particularly to Mr. Robert Henrichsen, Mrs. Linda Swickheimer, Mr. Charles A. Long, Miss Trebie Carlson and Miss Jacquelyn Dugey for their artistic talents which were indispensible in the preparation of the manuscript.

The tedious and ardous task of typing and retyping the many drafts and final manuscript has been in the capable hands of Mrs. Debbie A. Brunet, Mrs. Mary McCloy, Miss Pegi Murphy, Mrs. Carol Kern, and Mrs. Dorothy Austin; and we are deeply indebted to them for their loyalty, patience, and secretarial assistance, above and beyond the call of duty, without which, the manuscript could not have been completed. We are also indebted to Mrs. Shane Chaney for her many hours spent in searching out references for the manuscript.

Last, but not least, we would like to thank Ralph R. Shuffler, II, M.Dv. for his advice and assistance in reading the manuscript.

POISONOUS
PLANTS

POISONOUS PLANTS
Michael D. Ellis, M.S.

3

B.   Wild Plants of the Woods and/or Meadows

INTRODUCTION

In this chapter the more common poisonous plants are classified into two, somewhat arbitrary, categories. Several of the plants that are listed under the "House and Garden Plants" category are also found growing in a wild and uncultivated state; but an attempt has been made to place these plants into the category in which they are most usually found.

For the plants in the "Wild Plants of the Woods and/or Meadows" category a secondary classification is also provided. The areas of the state of Texas in which they are normally found are indicated utilizing the vegetational areas and information from *Texas Plants—A Checklist and Ecological Summary* by Frank Gould.* These areas are designated with the numbers corresponding to the vegetational areas indicated in Figure 1.

The botanical descriptions of these plants will offend most taxonomists, since in order to make the description more readily understandable to non-botanists, certain liberties have been taken in describing plant parts. It is hoped that these measures will make the descriptions more easily used by all persons reading them.

The chemical formulae appearing in this section of the book are reproduced with permission from *The Merck Index,* Eighth Ed.**

*Texas A&M Univ., Texas Agricultural Experiment Station, Bulletin MP-585/Revised, April 1969.
**Copyright 1968 by Merck & Co., Inc., Rahway, New Jersey.

Cultivated House
And Garden Plants

Caladium spp.	—	**CALADIUM, FANCY-LEAF CALADIUM** (Figs. 6, 7)
Colocasia spp.	—	**ELEPHANT EAR, DASHEEN** (Fig. 4)
Dieffenbachia spp.	—	**DUMBCANE, ELEPHANT EAR, DIEFFENBACHIA** (Fig. 2 a, b, c)
Monstera spp.	—	**SPLIT-LEAF PHILODENDRON, CERIMAN** (Fig. 5)
Philodendron spp.	—	**PHILODENDRON, ELEPHANT EAR** (Fig. 3 a, b, c, d)

DESCRIPTION:

Caladium spp. - **CALADIUM** - The multicolored leaves of the many horticultural varieties of this plant are easily recognizable. The valentine-shaped leaves usually attain 12 - 15 inches in length and display prominent venation that may be of numerous colors. Often the venation is a color different from that of the bulk of the leaf. These plants are frequently referred to incorrectly as colocasias.

Colocasia spp. - **ELEPHANT EAR** - The leaves of this genus can attain considerable size, ranging to 2 feet or more in length. Each leaf is supported by a single leaf stalk, which may be up to 5 feet in length. The leaves may be either multicolored or solid green, displaying prominent venation. One species of this group *Colocasia esculenta* ("Taro") has an edible tuber which is used to make poi in Hawaii and other Pacific islands. This edibility, however, does not extend to any other species of this plant.

Dieffenbachia spp. - **DUMBCANE** - This decorative large-leafed plant is native to tropical American climates but is found throughout the United States both as a house plant and in commercial establishments. The regularly segmented stems are fleshy, up to 1 inch or more in diameter, and normally attain a height of 3 to 6 feet; although older plants may be considerably larger. The leaves are basically dark green in color; although the many horticultural varieties have various spots, streaks, or a mottled appearance. These mottlings may be white, light or dark green, or greenish-yellow.

Monstera spp. - **SPLIT-LEAF PHILODENDRON** - This woody-stemmed climber has large (up to 3 feet) green, leathery leaves. The leaves are basically heart-shaped with prominent lobes and irregularly placed oblong holes throughout the leaf. They are frequently found both in homes and businesses.

9

Philodendron spp. - **PHILODENDRON** - There are hundreds of individual species of this plant, as well as many horticultural varieties of the individual species. Basically there are 3 different leaf styles. The first is a large (1 - 2 feet) and somewhat elongated, valentine-shaped leaf that is supported by a single stalk. It has prominent venation which may range in color from light green to white, to pink or red. The second type is a modification of the first, but the leaf is prominently notched or lobed. The common name "split-leaf" philodendron is apt. The third type is a climbing vine with relatively small valentine-shaped leaves, which are usually 3 to 6 inches long and may or may not be varigated.

GENERAL:

All of the plants described above are members of the *Arum* family and all contain essentially the same toxic constitutents (56, 57). Numerous cases of *Dieffenbachia* ingestion and its treatment have been reported in the scientific literature (31, 34, 66). The symptoms and treatment of the other members of this family parallel those of the *Dieffenbachia.*

The ingestion of any part of the plant will cause symptoms of poisoning. The entire plant contains needle-like crystals of calcium oxalate (29) and a proteinaceous substance (most probably a proteolytic enzyme or protease) (85), which produces severe irritation of any mucous membrane contacted. Seldom is the plant swallowed, due to the intense pain and burning sensation accompanying the mere biting of the leaf.

SYMPTOMATOLOGY:

Upon biting into any part of the plant an immediate burning sensation in the mouth is experienced. The intense irritation of the mucous membranes may produce severe edema and swelling of the tongue, lips, palate, and buccal surfaces. Copious salivation, a swollen tongue, along with the accompanying pain, and edema may lead to complete dysphagia or inability to swallow. The swollen state of the tongue or pharyngeal edema may physically inhibit respiration.

No specific systemic effects have been reported from the ingestion of these plants. This is most probably due to the fact that the local effect in the mouth of these noxious substances has limited the swallowing of the plant in any quantity. Should swallowing of the plant occur, intense esophageal and gastric irritation is possible. Dermatitis due to either handling of the plant or contact with its white milky juice has been reported in susceptible individuals.

Experimentally, the juice of *Dieffenbachia picta* produced both corneal and conjunctival damage. The juice caused corneal opacity in all of the test animals, although all but one eye had cleared by 72 hours (37). In a similar clinical report involving *D. seguine* juice, the corneal injury healed without any irreversible changes being noted (4).

PATHOLOGY:

Superficial necrosis of both the tongue and buccal mucosa may occur; as well as necrosis of the esophagus and stomach if the plant is swallowed. Local necrosis of the cornea is frequently produced if the juice of the plant is gotten in the eye.

TREATMENT:

Therapy includes both administering meperidine for the intense pain and rinsing of the mouth with water and aluminum-magnesium hydroxide suspension. Administration of either milk, or aluminum-magnesium hydroxide suspension for their soothing and demulcent effect may be helpful. Be alert for the possibility of performing a tracheostomy should the swollen tongue and throat severely hamper respiration. The edema usually begins to decrease in 2 - 4 days, and is essentially gone by 11 - 12 days. The associated pain may be quite severe and may not begin to abate for a week or more.

Experimentally, increased blood levels of histamine have been shown. Pretreatment with diphenhydramine provided considerable protection. Cortisone-treated animals displayed a delayed reaction with only a slight change in the total inflammatory response (37).

Ricinus communis — CASTOR BEAN, CASTOR OIL PLANT, PALMA CHRISTI
(Fig. 8 a, b, c, d)

DESCRIPTION:

This stout shrub-like herb is cultivated for its large dark green foliage. Although it is classified as an annual, in warmer climates it grows as a perennial and can attain heights of up to 12 feet. The large stems may be either green or dull red in color. Its large green leaves may be as broad as 1 to 3 feet, having from 5 to 11 clefts with toothed margins. The fruit is a capsule measuring about 1 inch in diameter and is covered with soft spines. Each capsule contains 3 black seeds, mottled with white or gray, which closely resemble ticks. Flowers appear at the ends of the upright branches. The flowers are white to rust colored.

GENERAL:

The toxicity of the castor bean arises from the presence of the toxalbumin ricin. It is both proteinaceous and antigenic and is composed of both hemagglutinating and toxic fractions (24). In solutions even as dilute as 1:1,000,000 ricin can produce hemagglutination and hemolysis of red blood cells (32). The hemagglutination produced by ricin appears to be due to its reaction with galactose and chemically similar sugars (33). One of the

11

substances that has been isolated from crystalline preparations of ricin is the toxic chemical ricinine.

As little as one seed can produce severe poisoning (52). One seed contains approximately 1 mg of ricin (5). The lethal dose of the seeds in children is probably about 3 to 6 seeds; while the adult fatal dose may be as high as 20 seeds. It should be noted, though, that fatalities have occurred with much smaller quantities (45). Allergic responses to the castor bean, its pollen, and products made from the bean are also known to occur.

RICININE

SYMPTOMATOLOGY:

The symptoms of poisoning from ingestion of the castor bean may be either immediate or may be delayed from several hours to several days. Initially, a burning sensation in the oral cavity may be seen. This is rapidly followed by nausea, persistent vomiting, abdominal pain, extreme thirst, and bloody diarrhea. Prostration, headache, weight loss, dullness of vision, dizziness, depression, and convulsions have all been reported. Oliguria may begin with uremia resulting. Hypotension, circulatory collapse, and finally death may occur (44, 57).

PATHOLOGY:

Postmortem examination reveals both hemorrhages and edema of the gastrointestinal tract, hemolysis, and degenerative changes in the liver and kidneys. Urinalysis shows casts, protein, red blood cells, and hemoglobin. Both elevated blood urea nitrogen and nonprotein nitrogen levels are frequently found. Hypomagnesemia may be present (5, 77).

TREATMENT:

Although there is no specific antidote for ricin poisoning, good medical management of patients on a symptomatic and supportive basis is the reason that the mortality rate is only about 5 to 6%. If the patient is seen prior to symptoms, induce repeated emesis and perform gastric lavage. Administer activated charcoal in large quantities and give a saline cathartic such as sodium sulfate. If symptoms are already apparent, dehydration may rapidly occur and adequate fluid and electrolyte therapy is necessary. Intoxication that does not lead to a fatality may produce symptoms which are readily apparent. A high carbohydrate diet may be a useful adjunct to therapy for minimizing liver damage (57).

Lantana spp. — LANTANA, HEN & CHICKS, BUNCHBERRY (Fig. 12 a, b, c, d)

DESCRIPTION:

This perennial plant which reaches a height of 3 - 5 feet is found throughout the state either growing wild or as a cultivated ornamental. The stems are widely branched, brittle at the joints; and bear irregularly scattered, weak, sharp spines. The leaves when crushed are highly aromatic and have a distinctive odor. The flowers are born in long-stalked clusters. They may be white, yellow, pink, orange, scarlet, or mixtures of colors depending on their species and variety. The clustered berries turn from green to dark blue or black as they mature. The lantana is found growing wild in vegetation areas 1, 2, 3, 4, 5, 6, 7, and 10.

GENERAL:

The toxic constituents of the lantana are lantadene A and several related triterpenoids. Although the entire plant contains these triterpenoids, it is the berries that are usually involved in most poisonings. The green berry is the most toxic. If small amounts of the plant or berries are ingested chronically it can result in the prevention of bilirubin conjugation, with retention jaundice and photosensitivity being the chief symptoms. However, in acute ingestions this does not appear to be the mechanism for the toxic symptoms.

LANTADENE A

SYMPTOMATOLOGY:

In acute poisonings the symptoms are delayed for a few hours. The symptoms include vomiting, diarrhea, weakness, ataxia, photophobia, and lethargy. Respiration is labored, slow, and deep. Pupils initially dilate, then become pinpoint. Deep tendon reflexes are depressed. The patient may become cyanotic and then comatose. Fatalities have occurred. The pattern of symptoms seem to vary somewhat with the different species of *Lantana*,

13

but most of the above symptoms are seen in all *Lantana* ingestions. In a reported death due to lantana poisoning of a 2 1/2 year old girl, the cause of death was described as acute pulmonary edema and neurocirculatory collapse (90).

PATHOLOGY:

Postmortem examination shows marked congestion of the lungs, mild congestion of the kidneys, and dilation of the small intestine.

TREATMENT:

Induce emesis if vomiting has not already occurred. Administer activated charcoal and perform gastric lavage as rapidly as possible. Lavage, up to 5 hours after ingestion, has proven lifesaving. Death has resulted only in those patients who were not initially lavaged (90). Saline catharsis is also indicated once the lavage is completed. Support respiration and administer oxygen. Corticosteroids have proven helpful if the patient must be hospitalized.

Cestrum diurnum   —   **DAY-BLOOMING JESSAMINE** (Fig. 10)

Cestrum nocturnum   —   **NIGHT-BLOOMING JESSAMINE** (Fig. 9)

DESCRIPTION:

Cestrum diurnum - **DAY-BLOOMING JESSAMINE** - The day-blooming jessamine is an evergreen shrub or tree; and may attain heights of up to 15 feet. Its leaves, which appear similar to the night-blooming variety, are usually about 3 1/2 - 4 inches long with smooth margins. Its quite fragrant, small, white, trumpet-shaped flowers open during the daytime. The fruit appears as a large number of berries that are greenish-white to a purplish-blue initially, but turn black as they mature.

Cestrum nocturnum - **NIGHT-BLOOMING JESSAMINE** - This evergreen shrub may reach 12 feet in height; and has shiny, thin leathery leaves. It has small, slender, tubular flowers which range from greenish-white to cream-colored. The flowers open only at night and are sweet-scented and very fragrant. The fruit is a small green berry which turns white as it matures.

GENERAL:

The berries of these plants are the parts that are usually involved in poisoning. The symptoms of poisoning due to ingestion of the berries may be somewhat confusing since the state of maturity of the berry determines the nature of the toxic substances. In the unripe berry, solanine

14

predominates as the toxic substance, while in the mature berry, tropane-related alkaloids (atropine-like) are most prevalent (44, 56, 57).

SYMPTOMATOLOGY:

The symptoms of poisoning due to solanine and atropine are somewhat parallel in that they both produce pupil dilation, dizziness, muscular weakness, restless or thrashing movements, and body temperature elevation. They differ in that solanine often produces symptoms of gastroenteritis, mental depression, salivation, sweating, and dyspnea. Headache is common. Stupefaction and loss of sensation have been reported. Atropine, on the other hand, produces a hot dry skin, a dry mouth, intense thirst, and symptoms due to central stimulation, including delerium, mania, and hallucinations. The pulse will be rapid and weak. There may be constipation and urinary retention (57).

TREATMENT:

Initial therapy is somewhat dependent on whether the predominant symptoms are those produced by atropine or solanine. If vomiting and other signs of gastrointestinal irritation are not present, induce emesis and perform gastric lavage. Administer activated charcoal and a saline cathartic (such as sodium sulfate).

Predominant symptoms of atropine intoxication call for the parenteral administration of the cholinergic drug, physostigmine. Since physostigmine penetrates the blood-brain barrier, it will antagonize the effects of atropine-like compounds both centrally as well as peripherally. A short-acting barbiturate may be indicated if the central excitation becomes severe. External cooling of the patient with cold water baths may help reduce the body temperature. Both the use of 1% pilocarpine ophthalmic solution and a dark room may help reduce the eye discomfort.

Should the symptoms indicate that solanine is the predominant toxic substance, treatment of the gastroenteritis is necessary. Demulcents such as either milk, aluminum hydroxide gel, magnesium oxide, or vegetable oil may be administered to aid in the reduction of the gastrointestinal irritation. The potential for renal involvement is present with proteinuria and hemoglobinuria usually being the first signs. Thereafter, treatment is primarily of a symptomatic and supportive nature.

Hedera helix — **ENGLISH IVY** (Fig. 11)

DESCRIPTION:

This climbing or creeping vine is commonly used as a wall or ground cover. The evergreen leaves are dark green in color, having a leathery feel and

15

appearance. The venation of the leaf is usually of a lighter green. It has small inconspicuous green flowers and occasionally small black berries.

GENERAL:

Although no cases of poisoning have been reported in the United States, the older European literature notes several cases of children being poisoned after ingestion of the berries. All parts of the plant are toxic, but their bitter taste discourages most would-be ingesters. At least two toxic constituents are present throughout the plant. One of these is a steroidal saponin, hederagenin, which is probably responsible for the systemic effects seen after ingestion (44, 56). This ivy also contains an as yet unidentified substance which causes dermatitis venenata (vesicular, edematous, erythematous) in sensitive individuals (41).

HEDERAGENIN

SYMPTOMATOLOGY:

Ingestion of small amounts of this plant will produce the local irritation associated with saponins that result in salivation, nausea, vomiting, abdominal pain, and severe diarrhea. Should absorption of the saponin occur, to a varying degree systemic effects of hemolysis will be seen, with the symptoms being proportional to the amount of hemolysis (77). Thus the patient may complain of headache, fever, thirst, and may be quite anxious. Facial rash and mydriasis may be present. Muscular weakness, ataxia, and incoordination may be present in more severe cases.

TREATMENT:

Induce emesis and administer activated charcoal. Perform gastric lavage, and adminster demulcents such as either milk, vegetable oil, or egg white to help protect the enteric mucosa. Treat for gastroenteritis and administer fluids and electrolytes to prevent dehydration. Thereafter, treatment is symptomatic and supportive.

Aleurites fordii — **TUNG NUT, TUNG OIL TREE** (Fig. 13)

DESCRIPTION:
   This introduced tree attains a height of about 30 feet. The flowers appear as terminal clusters and are white, streaked with red at the base. Large globular green fruits (a nut, 1 1/2 - 3 inches in diameter) ripen about September, yielding 3 - 7 thin-shelled oily seeds. The leaves are large, somewhat heart-shaped, and attain 5 - 10 inches in length.

GENERAL:
   This tree, which was introduced from China, has been widely planted throughout the southern United States for the seed oil which is used in the paint industry. The nut of this plant is the part most often involved in poisonings, although the entire plant is toxic. The whole ripe nut resembles a large walnut, while the unhulled seeds resemble Brazil nuts. The taste of the seed is not unpleasant initially, but is followed by a rancid after-taste. Several toxic fractions have been isolated, although it appears that the major toxic component is a heat-labile toxalbumin (7).

SYMPTOMATOLOGY:
   About 30 minutes to an hour after ingestion of the nut, gastrointestinal symptoms including nausea, vomiting, abdominal cramping, and diarrhea are seen. Tenesmus may be seen as well as intense thirst. Dehydration may occur due to the considerable loss of fluids and electrolytes. Both tachycardia and renal complications have been reported. Increased specific gravity of the urine, glucosuria, as well as epithelial cells and casts have been observed on urinalysis. More severe poisoning may be accompanied by symptoms of pyrexia, tachypnea, irregular respiration, mydriasis, depressed reflexes, and paresthesia. Cyanosis has also been observed. Severe headache may occur about 24 hours after the ingestion (7, 88, 89).

TREATMENT:
   If the patient is seen before the gastrointestinal symptoms appear, emesis should be induced and gastric lavage performed. Administer both activated charcoal and a demulcent such as milk or egg white. Magnesium sulfate appears to denature the toxic protein, although the mechanism of its action remains somewhat obscure (6). The management of the gastroenteritis is mainly of a symptomatic nature. Dehydration is frequent and requires appropriate fluid and electrolyte therapy. Recovery is usually complete within 24 to 48 hours.

Digitalis spp. — **DIGITALIS, FOXGLOVE** (Fig. 14 a, b, c,)

DESCRIPTION:

The foxglove is an erect biennial herb which can attain a height of 4 feet. It is cultivated in gardens and is found wild in both the northern United States and along the Pacific coast. The tall stalk bears large numbers of tubular, bell-shaped flowers during its second growing year. Spots are frequently found on the inside bottom surface of these flowers. The flowers vary in color depending on the variety (yellow, white, lavender, violet, and purple). Many seeds are borne in the small dry capsules, which are the fruit of the plant.

The leaf shape varies greatly, depending on the particular species. The shape can range from large, broad leaves up to 12 - 15 inches long, to small, narrow leaves about 3 - 4 inches long.

GENERAL:

The toxicity of this plant is due to the presence of varying concentrations of the cardioactive glycosides digitoxin, digoxin, gitoxin, and others. Drying does not diminish the concentrations of the glycosides present in the plant. Poisoning has resulted from children drinking the water from a vase containing the flowers (57). Eating of the leaves or seeds or sucking the flowers may also produce toxicity (44).

SYMPTOMATOLOGY:

After ingestion of the plant, there may be local irritation of the mouth and stomach followed frequently by emesis, abdominal pain, diarrhea, and persistent headache. These latter symptoms are most probably due to plant constitutents other than the cardioactive glycosides (57). As toxicity progresses, the cardiovascular symptoms become more apparent. The cardiac changes which have been reported include atrial fibrillation, ventricular premature contractions, partial to complete A-V block, and both atrial or ventricular fibrillation. Observed electrocardiographic changes include diminution of the amplitude or inversion of the T wave, depression of the S-T segment, shortening of the Q-T segment, prolongation of the P-R interval, and sometimes changes in the size and shape of the P wave (42).

TREATMENT:

If the symptoms of gastroenteritis are not present, induce emesis, perform gastric lavage, and administer activated charcoal. Follow this with a saline cathartic (*i.e.* sodium sulfate). Demulcents such as milk or vegetable oil may be of some help if the gastrointestinal symptoms are severe. If electrocardiographic analysis indicates digitalis intoxication, appropriate measures should be taken. There may be a lag period, although, before the cardiac manifestations are seen; depending on the particular plant ingested, its glycoside content, and the quantity of the glycoside absorbed from the intestinal tract.

The administration of potassium chloride either orally or intravenously may be indicated (57). Atropine sulfate and propranolol may be used to combat the exaggerated parasympathetic and sympathetic effects of the glycosides. The electrocardiogram should be monitored throughout the treatment period. Severe ventricular involvement may require therapy with Edetate (EDTA, Versenate) (57).

Rhododendron spp. — RHODODENDRON, AZALEA (Fig. 15 a, b, c)

DESCRIPTION:
Several wild species and numerous horticultural varieties of this plant are found throughout Texas. These rhododendrons or azaleas bear their showy flowers in numerous clusters. The flowers range from white to pink or rose in color, usually appearing in the early spring. Leaves are borne in clusters, frequently on terminal branches.

GENERAL:
Throughout the United States there are about 250 species of rhododendron and many horticultural varieties. Poisoning due to a number of these species has been well documented. Although specific evidence is lacking for a large number of these species; it is probable that many, if not most, of them are toxic. In all of the species tested the same toxic principle has been found (56). The substance which produces the toxic manifestations is the resinoid andromedotoxin, which has been crystallized and partially characterized chemically (91). All parts of the plant are toxic. Poisoning in children has resulted from either their sucking on the flowers or ingestion of a "tea" prepared from the leaves. Secondary poisonings due to the ingestion of honey made from the nectar of the rhododendron have also been reported (17).

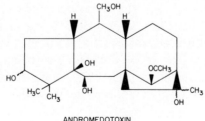

ANDROMEDOTOXIN

19

SYMPTOMATOLOGY:
    Ingestion of any part of the plant produces poisoning. Symptoms may be immediate or delayed for up to 6 hours. They include watering of the eyes and mouth, and nasal discharge. Anorexia, abdominal pain, nausea, and vomiting become apparent. The patient may complain of ataxia and loss of energy. Other symptoms include muscle weakness, progressive paralysis of the limbs, and convulsions. Both hypotension and slowed pulse rate are usually present. Fatalities have resulted from the ingestion of these plants (44, 87).

PATHOLOGY:
    Postmortem examination shows a nonspecific gastrointestinal irritation with some hemorrhage. Acute parenchymatous nephritis, tubular necrosis, as well as some albuminous hepatic degeneration have been seen (56).

TREATMENT:
    Induce vomiting and perform gastric lavage. Administer activated charcoal and give a saline cathartic such as sodium sulfate. Experimentally, the bradycardia has not responded to atropine (87). Severe hypotension may require the use of sympathomimetic agents. Thereafter, treatment is mainly supportive and symptomatic.

Euphorbia pulcherrima — **POINSETTIA, POINSETTA** (Fig. 17 a, b)

DESCRIPTION:
    This favorite Christmas plant is a small shrub or pot plant. It has large, dark green leaves measuring up to 6 inches or more in length, the margins of which are either smooth or may have coarse, shallow teeth. In the fall, the floral leaves become brightly colored and may be either bright red, pink, yellowish, or white. A white milky sap exudes from the plant whenever it is injured.

GENERAL:
    Although the poinsettia has a wide reputation for being a very toxic plant, its reputation is, for the most part, unjustly due. The validity of a 1919 report of a fatality in Hawaii due to the ingestion of a wild poinsettia by a 2 year old, now appears to be in some doubt (80). Ingestion of the leaves of this plant by small children has occurred frequently. Some do display symptoms. Sensitive individuals may experience contact dermatitis when they handle the leaf or contact the milky sap (30).

SYMPTOMATOLOGY:
    Ingestion of the poinsettia may produce some gastrointestinal irritation

20

with nausea, vomiting, and diarrhea occurring. There may be some blistering of the lips, tongue, or buccal surfaces due to contact with the sap. Blistering of the skin or dermatitis may also occur in sensitive individuals.

TREATMENT:
Induce emesis if vomiting has not already occurred. Administer a demulcent such as milk, aluminum hydroxide gel, *et cetera,* for its protective effect. Observe the patient and treat any other effects on a symptomatic basis.

Delphinium spp. — **DELPHINIUM, LARKSPUR, CROWFOOT** (Fig. 16 a, b, c)

DESCRIPTION:
This annual or perennial, erect, long stalked, branching herb is found throughout the state in many gardens. Several wild varieties are also found throughout Texas. The leaves of most of the cultivated forms are quite lacy. A prominent "spur" protrudes to the rear of the flower and makes for easy identification of this plant. There are several hundred different species of this plant with a variety of flower colors including blue, violet, pink, white, and yellow. Each flower when mature will bear many small (2 mm in diameter), black seeds which are covered with numerous tiny spines. The delphinium is found in vegetation areas 1, 2, 3, 4, 5, 6, 7, 8, 9 and 10.

GENERAL:
Wild forms of the larkspur, particularly in the western United States, are responsible for the death of numerous livestock. The entire plant is toxic, although the toxicity decreases somewhat in older plants. The seeds are the most toxic portion. They can be purchased at any seed store or nursery. Unfortunately, the seed package does not carry any indication as to the potential toxicity that the seed can produce if ingested. An old pharmaceutical preparation, "Larkspur Lotion", which was official in the 1950 edition of the National Formulary; was prepared from the seeds of this plant. The main use of larkspur lotion was in the treatment of head lice. The high toxicity and the ready absorption either orally or through abraded skin made its use too dangerous and it is no longer commercially available.
The toxicity of the larkspur is due primarily to the alkaloid delphinine and other related alkaloids. Delphinine is almost chemically identical to the very toxic alkaloid aconitine, which was used in medical antiquity for both neuralgia and as a cardiac depressant. The oral lethal dose of delphinine is approximately the same as that of aconitine (from 2 to 5 mg.).

21

OH
OCH₃
CH₃O
OCOC₆H₅
CH₃
N
OCOCH₃
CH₂
OCH₃
OCH₃

DELPHININE

OH
OCH₃
CH₃O
OCOC₆H₅
CH₃CH₂
OH
N
HO
OCOCH₃
CH₂
OCH₃
OCH₃

ACONITINE

SYMPTOMATOLOGY:

Ingestion of either this plant or its seeds produces a tingling feeling, then burning and inflammation of the mouth, lips, tongue, and pharynx followed by numbness. Paresthesia, beginning in the extremities, progresses until the entire body becomes involved. It is most intense in the facial areas innervated by the trigeminal nerve. This paresthesia is soon followed by numbness. Salivation, followed later by a dry mouth, nausea, and vomiting may be seen. Sweating may occur, although the skin remains cold and clammy. The patient may experience tinnitis, and may be irritable and confused. Intense headache is usually seen (57). Respiration becomes labored and pulmonary edema is possible.

Cardiovascular disturbances including hypotension and myocardial depression may be readily apparent. The cardiac arrhythmias, which have been difficult to manage with drug therapy, consist primarily of supraventricular tachycardia and conduction disturbances.

The respiratory failure that is seen in larkspur poisoning is most probably secondary to the cardiovascular disturbances and the concomitant circulatory failure (57, 84).

TREATMENT:

The signs of intoxication are rapid. Death may occur within less than 6 hours. Immediately perform gastric lavage with 1:5000 potassium permanganate and large volumes of water. Administer large quantities of activated charcoal followed by a saline cathartic (i.e. sodium sulfate). Be prepared to support respiration and monitor the patient's cardiovascular status frequently. Be prepared to treat any developing cardiac arrhythmias. Experimentally these arrhythmias have responded to intravenous calcium gluconate followed by magnesium sulfate (60).

Hydrangea macrophylla   —   **HYDRANGEA** (Fig. 19 a, b, c)

Pyrus sylvestris   —   **APPLE** (Fig. 18)
(Malus sylvestris)

DESCRIPTION:

Hydrangea macrophylla - **HYDRANGEA** - This large shrub may reach 10 feet in height. Although many horticultural varieties are available, they usually have the same general appearance. The leaves attain 6 or more inches in length and about 3 1/2 or 4 inches in width and have coarsely toothed margins. They are dark green above but have a fuzzy grayish underside. The small flowers are borne as large rounded clusters. They may be either white, pink, or blue in color.

Toxic Parts: The leaves and buds contain the cyanogenic glycoside, hydrangin (44).

Pyrus sylvestris - **APPLE** - This cultivated tree can reach 30 - 40 feet in height. The green leaves have finely serrated margins and attain a diameter of 1 - 4 inches. Various species of the apple tree produce apples of varying color including yellow, red, and a light green.

Toxic Parts: The seeds contain a cyanogenic glycoside and are toxic in large numbers.

GENERAL:

Although poisoning due to the ingestion of these plants is not common there have been reports in the literature of several cases of toxicity. Both plants contain cyanogenic glycosides and are capable of releasing hydrocyanic acid on alkaline hydrolysis. One case of poisoning due to the hydrangea resulted when the children of a family put the buds of the plant into a tossed salad. The end result was the poisoning of the entire family, although the predominant symptoms were of a gastrointestinal nature, namely nausea, vomiting, and diarrhea (56, 88). Ingestion of apple seeds in any quantity presents a dangerous situation. One reported case involved an adult male who considered apple seeds a delicacy and consumed a cupful over a short period of time. This case ended in fatality due to cyanide poisoning (56).

A number of variables effect the severity of the symptoms; the cyanogenic potential of the plant part, the free HCN concentration, the weight of the patient, the degree of wetness of the plant part or liquid consumed after ingestion, and the rapidity of HCN release in the patient's gastrointestinal tract. The elapsed time since the patient's last meal and the components of the meal are important, since the presence of other substances in the gastrointestinal tract tends to retard absorption of the cyanide. Also, since

23

the HCN is a very reactive substance, many chemically inactivating reactions may occur in the gastrointestinal tract if other food substances are present (56).

SYMPTOMATOLOGY:

Frequently the first signs seen are those due to gastroenteric distress. Nausea, vomiting, abdominal pain, and diarrhea may be seen. Further symptoms of cyanide (prussic acid) poisoning include dyspnea, muscular weakness, ataxia, and fibrillary twitchings. Stupor, coma, and convulsions either before or after loss of consciousness, may be seen.

TREATMENT:

Once symptoms have begun, treatment must be rapid if death is to be avoided. Treat initially for the gastrointestinal distress that is seen in the early stages of cyanogenic glycoside ingestion. Induce emesis if it has not already occurred. First, administer large quantities of activated charcoal and then perform gastric lavage until the lavage solution is clear. Although the charcoal will adsorb considerable amounts of the HCN, it will also release it slowly in the alkaline media of the intestinal tract. Administer a saline cathartic such as sodium sulfate.

If the other symptoms of poisoning are already present, therapy consists of inducing relative methemoglobinemia with amyl and sodium nitrite. Have the patient inhale amyl nitrite while preparing a 3% sodium nitrite solution. (CAUTION: Nitrites can produce severe hypotension if injected too rapidly, as well as headache, vomiting, syncope, and unconsciousness.)

In adults, administer 10 ml of a 3% (300 mg/10 ml) sodium nitrite solution intravenously at the rate of 2 - 5 ml/minute. Draw blood for the determination of hemoglobin and methemoglobin concentrations. As soon as the nitrite injection is finished, administer intravenously 50 ml of a 25% (12.5 Gm/50 ml) solution of sodium thiosulfate. Administer oxygen and support the patient's respiration. Since the symptoms of poisoning may reappear, be prepared to repeat the sodium nitrite and sodium thiosulfate administration; the dose being one-half that of the initial dosage. The methemoglobin concentration produced by both of these sodium nitrite injections should not be greater than 40% of the initial hemoglobin concentration; otherwise a state of anoxia may put the patient's life in jeopardy (10).

In children the dosage of nitrite becomes somewhat more critical due to their relatively smaller hemoglobin concentration. Usually it is safe to administer 10 mg/kg (0.3 ml/kg) of the 3% sodium nitrite solution, then obtain blood for hemoglobin and methemoglobin concentrations. The following schedule should be followed for the *initial* dose of the antidotes (bearing in mind that a repeat administration of one-half the initial dose may be necessary if symptoms reappear) (10).

24

| *Hemoglobin | Initial Dose - NaNO2** | | Initial Dose of 25% |
Gm/100 ml	(mg/kg)	(ml of 3% of soln/kg)	Na Thiosulfate (ml/kg)**
7.0	5.8	0.19	0.95
8.0	6.6	0.22	1.10
9.0	7.5	0.25	1.25
10.0	8.3	0.27	1.35
11.0	9.1	0.30	1.50
12.0	10.0	0.33	1.65
13.0	10.8	0.36	1.80
14.0	11.6	0.39	1.95

*Reproduced with permission from Pediatrics 46:793 (1970) by C. M. Berlin, Jr.

**(The initial dose of sodium nitrite will produce 26.8% methemoglobinemia. The sodium thiosulfate dose is based on the adult ratio: 5 ml of 25% sodium thiosulfate to 1 ml of 3% sodium nitrite.)

Children over 25 Kg who are not anemic may receive the adult dose of the antidotes.

Although a cyanide antidote kit containing the above indicated antidotes is commercially available (Eli Lilly and Co., Indianapolis, Ind.), if the sterilized solutions cannot be obtained, do not hesitate to use nonsterile ones. The time factor between onset of symptoms and fatality may not be very great. The administration of these specific antidotes may prove the difference between life and death.

Convallaria majalis — LILY-OF-THE-VALLEY (Fig. 20 a, b)

DESCRIPTION:

This small, perennial plant is indigenous to the northeastern part of the United States, although it can be obtained through florists and nurseries throughout the country. It has two oblong-oval leaves and a central stalk which bears several small, white, nodding, bell-shaped flowers which are very fragrant. The fruits, produced infrequently, are about 1/2 inch in diameter and are bright red to orange-red.

GENERAL:

All parts of the plant, whether green or dried, are poisonous and contain the cardioactive glycosides convallarin, convallamarin, and convallatoxin. Chemically these glycosides are very similar to the digitalis glycosides. Ingestion of only a portion of the leaf may prove fatal. Minimal lethal dose by injection has been shown experimentally to be less than 0.2 mg/kg (39). The chemical structure of convallamarogenin (convallamarin without its attached sugar moiety) is given below.

25

CONVALLAMAROGENIN

SYMPTOMATOLOGY:

The symptoms of poisoning by the lily - of - the - valley parallel those found in digitalis overdose. Signs of toxicity appear more rapidly with *Convallaria* poisoning than in digitalis intoxication (92). After ingestion of the plant, there may be local irritation of the mouth and stomach followed frequently by emesis, abdominal pain, diarrhea, and persistent headache. These latter symptoms are most probably due to plant constituents other than the cardioactive glycosides (57). As toxicity progresses, the cardiovascular symptoms become more apparent. Cardiac changes including atrial fibrillation, ventricular premature contractions, partial to complete A-V block, and atrial or ventricular fibrillation have been reported. Electrocardiographic changes including diminution of the amplitude or inversion of the T wave, depression of the S-T segment, shortening of the Q-T segment, prolongation of the P-R interval, and sometimes changes in the size and shape of the P wave have all been observed (42).

TREATMENT:

If emesis has not already occurred, induce vomiting, perform gastric lavage, and administer activated charcoal. Follow this with a saline cathartic such as sodium sulfate. Demulcents such as milk or vegetable oil may be of some benefit if the gastrointestinal symptoms are severe. Otherwise, therapy parallels that for digitalis intoxication when an electrocardiographic analysis so indicates. There may be a lag period, although, before the cardiac manifestations are seen, depending on the amount of plant ingested, its glycoside content, and the quantity of the glycoside absorbed from the intestinal tract.

If the cardiovascular effects are apparent the administration of potassium chloride either orally or intravenously may be indicated (57). Atropine sulfate and propranolol may be used to combat the exaggerated parasympathetic and sympathetic effects of the glycosides. The electrocardiogram should be monitored throughout the treatment period. Severe ventricular involvement may require therapy with Edetate (EDTA, Versenate) (57).

Lathyrus odoratus — **SWEET PEA** (Fig. 21 a, b)

DESCRIPTION:
   This popular climbing vine is a favorite among gardeners for its sweet-smelling blossoms. The clusters of flowers may be white, pink, lavender, red, or purple. The leaves are slightly elongated ovals with pointed tips, appearing in pairs on the winged green stems. Small, hard, green peas about 1/4 inch in diameter are borne in green seed pods.

GENERAL:
   The toxic principle of the sweet pea is beta - (gamma - L - glutamyl) - aminopropionitrile. It is localized primarily in the pea or seed of the plant. Once ingested this compound may be converted *in vivo* to beta-aminopropionitrile, which appears to be the substance responsible for the toxic symptoms. When the seed is ingested chronically, as in India where it makes up part of the native diet, it causes skeletal deformities due to inhibition of cross-linking in the formation of collagen. In the development of vascular wall, elastic fiber formation is inhibited, thus lowering the resistance to vascular wall stretching. The end result is a predisposition to vascular aneurysms. During pregnancy, the developing fetus is especially sensitive to the poison (56).

SYMPTOMATOLOGY:
   The acute toxicity of sweet pea ingestion manifests itself as a paralytic syndrome; although the pea has to be consumed in rather large quantities before symptoms become apparent. Other symptoms of toxicity include a slowed and weakened pulse, depressed and weakened respiration, and convulsions (44).

TREATMENT:
   If large quantities of the seed have been ingested, induce emesis and perform gastric lavage. Administer activated charcoal and a saline cathartic. Thereafter, symptomatic and supportive therapy is indicated.

Ipomoea violacea — **MORNING GLORY (Varieties: "FLYING SAUCERS", "HEAVENLY BLUES", "PEARLY GATES")** (Fig. 24)

DESCRIPTION:
   This twining vine is a favorite of many gardeners. The heart-shaped leaf reaches about 3 inches in length and 2 1/2 inches in width. Colors of the funnel-shaped flowers vary depending on the variety - the "Pearly Gates" being white, the "Heavenly Blues" being bright blue usually with a white

center, and the "Flying Saucers" being basically white streaked with blue or light purple. Small (about 1/4 inch long), dark brown seeds are produced.

GENERAL:
The seeds of the morning glory, and these three varieties in particular, have been involved in several ingestions. There are small quantities of several alkaloids (up to 0.04%) (2) chemically related to lysergic acid diethylamide (LSD) in all of these seeds. The alkaloids include lysergic acid amide (lysergamide), isoergine, elymoclavine, and several others (27). Many of the seed packaging companies are now coating these morning glory seeds with a nauseant in an attempt to discourage their ingestion. The presence of insecticides on the seeds may possibly alter some of the symptoms seen. Most cases of ingestion involve 200 to 300 seeds and this number is quite sufficient to produce hallucinogenic effects.

LYSERGAMIDE

LYSERGIDE   (LSD)

SYMPTOMATOLOGY:
The ingestion of morning glory seeds produces only some of the symptoms classically seen in LSD ingestion cases. Hallucinogenic symptoms have included depersonalization, visual and tactile hallucination-like states, memory losses, and feelings of transcendence. The initial hallucinogenic effects may last for over 8 hours, then completely disappear, only to reoccur later, sometimes after several days. Physiologic effects including nausea, anorexia, abdominal discomfort, explosive diarrhea, frequent urination, and depressed deep tendon reflexes have been reported (22, 48).

TREAMENT:
If the patient is seen prior to the development of hallucinogenic effects, induction of vomiting is indicated. Perform gastric lavage and administer activated charcoal. Follow this with a saline cathartic (*i.e.,* sodium sulfate). If hallucinogenic effects are already apparent, chlorpromazine may provide the patient with some relief. Psychiatric care, as well as symptomatic and supportive treatment are indicated thereafter.

Hyacinthus orientalis	—	HYACINTH (Fig. 25)
Ilex spp.	—	HOLLY, CHRISTMAS HOLLY (Fig. 22 a, b)
Ilex vomitoria	—	YAUPON, YAUPON HOLLY, YOUPON (Fig. 23)
Iris spp.	—	IRIS (Fig. 26)
Ligustrum spp.	—	LIGUSTRUM, COMMON PRIVET, WAXED LEAF LIGUSTRUM (Fig. 27 a, b)
Narcissus spp.	—	NARCISSUS, DAFFODIL, JONQUIL (Fig. 28)
Poinciana gilliesii (*Caesalpinia gilliesii*)	—	POINCIANA, BIRD-OF-PARADISE (Fig. 29 a, b)
Wisteria spp.	—	WISTERIA (Fig. 30 a, b, c)

DESCRIPTION:

Hyacinthus orientalis - **HYACINTH** - This common garden or pot plant has 1 or 2 erect stalks from which numerous flowers bloom. Many colors are available including pink, white, yellow, and blue.
Toxic Part: The bulb is the most dangerous portion, although the leaves and flowers may be harmful if eaten in any quantity. It can also cause allergic contact dermatitis in sensitive individuals (44).

Ilex spp. - **HOLLY** - These evergreen hollies with their bright red berries are a favorite for Christmas decorating. Most species can reach a height of 40 - 50 feet if allowed to grow, although usually they are kept trimmed and used as ornamental hedges. The leaves are usually dentate with sharp spines on the margins, and may appear either dull or dark and shiny green. Many horticultural varieties of holly have been prepared and their leaf shapes may vary considerably.
Toxic Part: Ingestion of the bright red berries, which contain the bitter principle, ilicin, are responsible for several poisonings in children (44, 57).

Ilex vomitoria - **YAUPON** - This shrub or tree-like evergreen is found in great abundance, particularly in the central and eastern portions of the state. Its small (to 1 1/2 inches), slightly toothed leaves contain no toxic substance and have been used in brewing of a mild "tea". The fruits of this shrub consist of clusters of small scarlet berries. The yaupon is found in vegetation areas 1, 2, 3, 6 and 7.
Toxic Part: The bright red berries are the poisonous parts of this plant (44).

Iris spp. - **IRIS** - This popular garden plant with its long, erect, sword-shaped leaves and characteristic flower is easily recognized. The leaves are somewhat fleshy and have parallel venation. There are about 200 or more varieties of this plant. The flower colors are numerous including white, yellow, blue, purple, lavender, and others.
Toxic Part: The rootstalk or rhizome ("bulb") of this plant is the portion involved in poisoning. Whether all the species of the iris are toxic or not is not known. The fact that there are several known toxic members make the others suspect. Allergic contact dermatitis has been known to occur in sensitive individuals (44, 57).

Ligustrum spp. - **LIGUSTRUM** - This dark green shrub or small tree, some species of which are evergreen, is widely used as a hedge and lends itself quite well to trimming and shaping. The leaves can range from 1 - 6 inches long depending on the species. Some horticultural varieties have varigated margins of a light yellow, gold, or white. The small white flowers appear as terminal, somewhat pyramid-shaped clusters, and are followed by large numbers of dark blue-to-black berry-like fruit.
Toxic Part: The berries and possibly the leaves contain toxic substances as yet uncharacterized. Fatalities in children have been reported.

Narcissus spp. - **NARCISSUS** - Many varieties of this common garden plant abound. The basic shape of the flower consists of 6 - 7 flat, basal petals and a central "cup" of petals which projects forward. The "cup" petals may be either the same or a color different than that of the basal petals. The flowers may be solid yellow, white, or apricot. Color combination of the basal and "cup" petals include white with orange, yellow with orange, white with pink, and yellow with red-orange.
Toxic Part: The bulb is the most dangerous part. Allergic contact dermatitis has been reported in sensitive individuals (56, 57).

Poinciana gilliesii - **POINCIANA** - This showy shrub or small tree is grown either as an outdoor perennial or large pot plant. It has alternate leaves with numerous small leaflets. The large flowers are light yellow with long exserted red stamens. A flat seed pod measuring 4 inches long and 3/4 inch wide is produced and contains 5 - 7 seeds (44, 57). The poinciana is found in vegetation areas 5, 6, 7 and 8.
Toxic Part: Ingestion of the green seed pods has produced toxicity in children (3).

Wisteria spp. - **WISTERIA** - This woody climbing vine, shrub, or small tree in cultivated forms, is widely planted for its showy racemes (hanging clusters) of flowers. The flowers usually are various shades of blue; although there are varieties which have white, pink, or purple flowers. In early summer a flat velvety seed pod; varying in length from 2 - 5 inches depending on the variety, and containing 1 - 3 seeds; is produced.

Toxic Part: The whole pods or the seeds, if ingested, will produce rapid signs of poisoning (44, 49, 57).

GENERAL:

The above plants all contain irritant properties, which for the most part remain unidentified. The onset of symptoms produced by the ingestion of the indicated toxic portions of these plants is usually relatively rapid, frequently occurring within 30 minutes to 1 hour. Symptoms are usually quite violent, but frequently recovery has begun by 24 hours and is essentially complete in 48 hours.

SYMPTOMATOLOGY:

Rapid onset of symptoms; including nausea, abdominal pain, severe vomiting, and diarrhea, which may range from mild to violent, are seen. It is not uncommon for the vomitus to be tinged with blood or bile. Severe dehydration can rapidly occur and must be guarded against.

TREATMENT:

If vomiting has not already occurred or has not been sufficient to empty the stomach, emesis should be induced. Demulcents such as milk, vegetable oil, or egg white should be administered before gastric lavage is performed. Administer activated charcoal. Further administration of a demulcent is indicated. Replace lost fluids and electrolytes. The administration of chlorpromazine for its antiemetic action may provide the patient with some relief.

Melia azedarach — **CHINABERRY TREE, CHINA TREE, TEXAS UMBRELLA TREE** (Fig. 31 a, b, c)

DESCRIPTION:

This tree grows to about 45 feet tall, bearing small light purple flowers during the mid-spring. The large leaves are composed of numerous small (1 1/4 - 2 inch) serrated leaflets. The fruit of this tree is a small (1/2 inch), smooth, ovoid drupe ("berry") which turns from green to yellow in the early autumn. Large numbers of these "berries" are produced. They are borne in large conspicuous clusters which remain on the tree long after the leaves are gone. The chinaberry tree is found growing wild in vegetation areas 2, 3, and 4.

GENERAL:

The toxicity of this plant varies considerably with the growing conditions and subvarieties. Some are quite poisonous while others have been eaten with impunity. This fact notwithstanding, all chinaberry ingestions should be treated as though poisoning is imminent. The toxic principals have not been completely characterized, although there is a saponin and a toxic alkaloid present throughout the plant. All parts of the plant are capable of causing poisoning, but it is the berries that are usually involved (56, 57). As few as 6 to 8 berries has produced fatality in young children (44). Poisoning in animals has been shown to cause fatty degeneration of the kidneys and liver (56).

SYMPTOMATOLOGY:

Symptoms of poisoning may be rapid or delayed for several hours after the ingestion. Two types of symptoms have been seen with ingestion of this plant. The irritant properties produce nausea, vomiting, and often bloody diarrhea. Depression or excitement as well as dyspnea, syncope, ataxia, mental confusion, and sometimes stupor have also been reported. Sweating, pupil dilatation, labored respirations, varying degrees of paralysis, and convulsions may occur (44, 57).

TREATMENT:

If vomiting and through emptying of the stomach has not already occurred, induction of emesis is indicated. Perform gastric lavage and administer activated charcoal. A saline cathartic (*i.e.,* sodium sulfate) should be given. Severe gastrointestinal irritation may be helped by the administration of demulcents such as milk, egg white, or vegetable oil. Prolonged vomiting and diarrhea may produce dehydration and shock with appropriate fluid and electrolyte replacement being necessary.

Nerium oleander — OLEANDER (Fig. 32 a, b, c)

DESCRIPTION:

This evergreen woody shrub ranges in height from 5 to 25 feet. It has numerous short-stalked leaves, 3 - 10 inches in length, that are narrow and leathery. The leaves are pointed at the tip, dull dark green in color, smooth on the margin, and have a lighter-colored prominent midrib. The flowers are clustered at the end of the branches and may be various shades of white, pink, yellow, rose, or dark red.

GENERAL:

All parts of the plant, whether green or dried, are poisonous. They contain the cardioactive glycosides oleandroside, oleandrin, and nerioside. Poisoning has occurred from chewing of the leaves or flowers, drinking water from vases that contained the flowers, and using the stems either as skewers for roasting hot dogs or as a stirring utensil for food or drink. Ingestion of a single leaf has produced fatalities (88). Poisoning in children do not occur frequently, most probably due to the bitter taste and burning sensation produced when the leaf is chewed.

SYMPTOMATOLOGY:

The symptoms of poisoning by oleander parallel those of digitalis overdose. After chewing the plant, there is local irritation of the mouth and stomach. This is frequently followed by emesis, abdominal pain, diarrhea, and persistent headache. These latter symptoms are most probably due to plant constituents other than the cardioactive glycosides (57). As the toxicity progresses, there is mental depression, visual disturbances, mydriasis, peripheral neuritis, fatigue, muscular weakness, and respiratory depression (13, 88). Cardiac changes including atrial fibrillation, ventricular premature contractions, partial to complete A-V block, and atrial or ventricular fibrillation have been reported. Electrocardiographic changes including diminution of the amplitude or inversion of the T wave, depression of the S-T segment, shortening of the Q-T segment, prolongation of the P-R interval, and sometimes changes in the size and shape of the P wave have all been observed (13).

OLEANDRIN

TREATMENT:

If emesis has not already occurred, induce vomiting, perform gastric lavage, and administer activated charcoal. Follow this with a saline cathartic such as sodium sulfate. Demulcents such as milk or vegetable oil may be of

33

some benefit if the gastrointestinal symptoms are severe. Otherwise, therapy parallels that for digitalis intoxication if the electrocardiographic analysis so indicates. There may be a lag period, although, between ingestion and the time when the cardiac manifestations are evident, depending on the amount of plant ingested, its glycoside content, and the quantity of the glycoside absorbed from the intestinal tract.

If the cardiovascular effects are apparent, the administration of potassium chloride either orally or intravenously may be indicated (57). Atropine sulfate and propranolol may be used to combat the exaggerated parasympathetic and sympathetic effects of the glycosides. The electrocardiogram should be monitored throughout the treatment period. Severe ventricular involvement may require therapy with Edetate (EDTA, Versenate) (57).

Podocarpus macrophylla — JAPANESE YEW, SOUTHERN YEW TREE
(Fig. 41 a, b)

DESCRIPTION:

This cultivated tree is often trimmed as a hedge but can attain 40 feet in height. The dense leaves are both long (2 - 5 inches) and narrow (about 1/3 inch) and are a dark lustrous green with a distinct light green midrib. Light blue berries appear in the early summer. Proximal to the harder blue berry is another, more fleshy fruit ("berry") which turns from green to red to dark purple as it matures.

GENERAL:

These berries, both the blue and the fleshy purple ones, are the most frequently ingested parts. The fleshy purple berries are frequently mistaken for grapes by young children, and therefore, may be eaten in relatively large numbers. The leaves of this tree are also reported to produce symptoms. This yew should not be confused with another species of evergreen which is also known as the Japanese Yew. This latter species, *Taxus,* has much smaller leaves and a red fleshy berry. The *Taxus* berry resembles somewhat a stuffed olive, with the red fleshy pulp surrounding a dark brown seed that is visible from the end of the berry. The *Taxus* Yew is indigenous to the east coast but may be found as far south as South Carolina. However, it is not normally found in Texas. The seeds and leaves of this Yew *(Taxus)* are also toxic and have resulted in fatalities. Ingestion of the seeds produces initial gastroenteritis; but once the toxin is absorbed, the myocardial electrical conduction is affected. This results in hypotension, slowed and irregular pulse, and finally respiratory depression (47).

SYMPTOMATOLOGY:
Ingestion of either the harder blue berry or the fleshy purple berry of the Japanese or Southern Yew *(Podocarpus macrophylla)* produces primarily symptoms of gastrointestinal irritation. Nausea, vomiting, and diarrhea frequently occur and may be severe. No other symptoms of systemic toxicity have been observed.

TREATMENT:
Induce emesis if vomiting and other signs of gastrointestinal irritation are not already present. Gastric lavage and administration of activated charcoal followed by a saline cathartic are indicated. Demulcents such as milk or egg white may help relieve the gastrointestinal distress. Treatment thereafter is symptomatic and supportive.

Prunus americana — **AMERICAN PLUM, WILD PLUM** (Fig. 38)

Prunus armeniaca — **APRICOT** (Fig. 40)

Prunus caroliniana — **CHERRYLAUREL, CAROLINA CHERRYLAUREL** (Fig. 35)

Prunus cerasus — **CULTIVATED CHERRY** (Fig. 39)

Prunus persica — **PEACH** (Fig. 37)

Prunus serotina — **WILD BLACK CHERRY** (Fig. 34)

Prunus virginiana — **CHOKE CHERRY** (Fig. 36)

DESCRIPTION:
Prunus americana - **PLUM** - This coarse shrub or small tree can reach up to 24 feet in height. The relatively thin (1 1/2 to 2 inch) leaves grow 2 to 5 inches long and have sharply serrated margins. The fruit, 1 to 1 1/4 inches in diameter, may be either yellow or red.

Prunus armeniaca - **APRICOT** - This cultivated tree can reach 20 to 30 feet tall. It has light green, finely serrated leaves which measure about 3 inches long and 2 - 2 1/2 inches wide. The mature golden yellow fruit, which may reach 2 inches in diameter, has a flattened seed stone.

Prunus caroliniana - **CHERRYLAUREL** - This tree is an evergreen that can reach 40 feet in height. The shiny leaves are a dark green on top and a lighter

35

green on the underside (2 to 5 inches long and 3/4 to 1 1/2 inches wide). The leaf margins may be either smooth or sparsely serrated. Crushing the leaf produces an aromatic odor, although it is quite bitter to the taste. The shiny black fruits have a thick skin and a thin fleshy portion. The cherrylaurel is found growing wild in vegetation area 1.

Prunus cerasus - **CHERRY** - The red to dark red globose fruit of this tree is familiar to anyone who frequents a grocery store. The green leaves are serrated and are about 4 inches long and 2 inches wide. Some species of cultivated cherries have leaves with smooth margins. The fruit stones are small and round, containing an even smaller seed pit.

Prunus persica - **PEACH** - This small cultivated tree has long (to 6 inches) light green leaves. The leaves have serrated margins and appear after the pink blossoms have faded. The fuzzy characteristic fruit which ripens to a golden yellow contains a deeply sculptured seed. Inside the hard seed coat is a smaller, very bitter flavored seed pit.

Prunus serotina - **WILD BLACK CHERRY** - This tree ranges to 100 feet in height. The dark green, shiny leaf blade is 2 to 6 inches long and 1 to 2 inches wide and tastes quite bitter if chewed. The paler green underside of the leaf is characterized by many fine, light orange plant hairs clustered around the base of the midrib. Leaf margins are finely serrated. During June to October the fruit (1/3 to 1/2 inch in diameter) matures and is black, juicy, and bittersweet. The wild black cherry is found in vegetation areas 1, 2, 3 and 4.

Prunus virginiana - **CHOKE CHERRY** - This large shrub or small tree has dark gray to brownish-black bark. The leaves are sharply serrated, a dark and shiny green color above with a paler underside. They range in size up to 4 inches long and 2 inches wide and have a strong odor when crushed. Small 1/4 to 1/3 inch cherries ripen in late summer and are scarlet to dark red or nearly black in color. The just barely edible fruit flesh is juicy, but bitter and astringent. The choke cherry is found growing wild in vegetation areas 8, 9 and 10.

GENERAL:

All the members of the genus *Prunus* contain high concentrations of cyanogenic glycosides throughout the entire plant, including the leaves, stems, bark, and seed pits. The fleshy pulp of the fruit is the only portion of the plant that does not contain these glycosides (56). The toxic glycosides include amygdalin, prulaurasin, and prunasin all of which are hydrolyzed rapidly in an alkaline media via the reaction:

O—(GLUCOSE)$_2$ OH   O

AMYGDALIN   BENZALDEHYDE   CYANIDE

Since an alkaline medium is required for rapid hydrolysis of the glycosides, there may be a lag time between ingestion and the first signs of toxicity. Once the symptoms begin, their progress is rapid.

The lethal dose of hydrocyanic (prussic) acid in adults is approximately 50 mg. (44), although as little as 20 mg. has produced fatality in children. There is little difference between the toxic and lethal blood levels of cyanide. The seed kernels (pits) of these plants are particularly high in cyanide (apricot - 0.1 - 2.8 mg/Gm; peach - 0.6 - 1.6 mg/Gm) (56, 72). The leaves also contain sizable concentrations of cyanide, ranging from 1.4 - 3.7 mg/Gm (1). Thus the potential for poisoning is great should a child ingest either a number of leaves or from 2 to 5 seed kernels.

Cyanide produces its toxicity by inhibiting cytochrome oxidase, the terminal catalytic enzyme system in the process of cellular respiration. Blood oxygen tensions are not altered in cyanide poisoning, although the ability of oxygen to dissociate from hemoglobin is somewhat impaired; therefore, oxygen therapy is a valuable adjunct in the treatment of cyanide poisoning (42).

A number of variables effect the severity of the symptoms; including, the cyanogenic potential of the plant part, the free HCN concentration, the weight of the patient, the degree of wetness of the plant or the amount of liquid consumed after ingestion, and the rapidity of HCN release in the patient's gastrointestinal tract. The elapsed time since the patient's last meal and what the meal consisted of is important, since the presence of other substances in the gastrointestinal tract tends to retard absorption of the cyanide. Also since HCN is a very reactive substance, many chemically inactivating reactions may occur in the gastrointestinal tract if other food substances are present (56).

SYMPTOMATOLOGY:

The symptoms of poisoning are those produced by hydrocyanic (prussic) acid and are the same as cyanide poisoning from any source. The onset is usually rapid with few or no forewarning signs. The usual sequence of symptoms include vomiting, dyspnea, muscular weakness, ataxia, and fibrillary twitchings. Stupor, coma, and convulsions, either before or after loss of counsciousness, may be seen.

TREATMENT:

Once symptoms have begun, treatment must be rapid if death is to be avoided. Treat initially for the gastrointestinal distress that is seen in the early stages of cyanogenic glycoside ingestion. Induce emesis if it has not already occurred. First, administer large quantities of activated charcoal and then perform gastric lavage until the lavage solution is clear. Although the charcoal will adsorb considerable amounts of the HCN, it will also release it slowly in the alkaline media of the intestinal tract. Administer a saline cathartic such as sodium sulfate.

If the other symptoms of poisoning are already present, therapy consists of inducing relative methemoglobinemia with amyl and sodium nitrite. Have the patient inhale amyl nitrite while preparing a 3% sodium nitrite solution. (CAUTION: Nitrites can produce severe hypotension if injected too rapidly, as well as headache, vomiting, syncope, and unconsciousness.)

In <u>adults</u>, administer 10 ml. of a 3% (300 mg/10 ml) sodium nitrite solution intravenously at the rate of 2 - 5 ml/minute. Draw blood for the determination of hemoglobin and methemoglobin concentrations. As soon as the nitrite injection is finished, administer intravenously 50 ml. of a 25% (12.5 Gm/50 ml) solution of sodium thiosulfate. Administer oxygen and support the patient's respiration. The symptoms of poisoning may reappear; therefore, be prepared to repeat the sodium nitrite and sodium thiosulfate administration, the dose being one-half that of the initial dosage. The methemoglobin concentration produced by both of these sodium nitrite injections should not be greater than 40% of the initial hemoglobin concentration; otherwise a state of anoxia may put the patient's life in jeopardy (10).

In <u>children</u>, the dosage of nitrite becomes somewhat more critical due to their relatively smaller hemoglobin concentrations. Usually it is safe to administer 10 mg/kg (0.3 ml/kg) of the 3% sodium nitrite solution, then obtain blood for hemoglobin and methemoglobin concentrations. The following schedule should be followed for the *initial* dose of the antidotes (bearing in mind that a repeat administration of one-half the initial dose may be necessary if symptoms reappear) (10).:

*Hemoglobin Gm/100 ml	Initial Dose - NaNO2** (mg/kg)	Initial Dose - NaNO2** (ml of 3% soln/kg)	Initial Dose of 25% Na Thiosulfate (ml/kg)**
7.0	5.8	0.19	0.95
8.0	6.6	0.22	1.10
9.0	7.5	0.25	1.25
10.0	8.3	0.27	1.35
11.0	9.1	0.30	1.50

*Hemoglobin Gm/100 ml	Initial Dose - NaNO$_2$** (mg/kg)	(ml of 3% soln/kg)	Initial Dose of 25% Na Thiosulfate (ml/kg)**
12.0	10.0	0.33	1.65
13.0	10.8	0.36	1.80
14.0	11.6	0.39	1.95

*Reproduced with permission from Pediatrics 46:793 (1970) by C. M. Berlin, Jr.

**(The initial dose of sodium nitrite will produce 26.8% methemoglobinemia. The sodium thiosulfate dose is based on the adult ratio: 5 ml of 25% sodium thiosulfate to 1 ml of 3% sodium nitrite.)

Children over 25 Kg who are not anemic may receive the adult dose of the antidotes.

Although a cyanide antidote kit containing the above indicated antidotes is commercially available (Eli Lilly and Co., Indianapolis, Ind.), if the sterilized solutions cannot be obtained, do not hesitate to use nonsterile ones. The time factor between onset of symptoms and fatality may not be very great. The administration of these specific antidotes may prove the difference between life and death.

Sapium sebiferum — **CHINESE TALLOW TREE, TALLOW TREE**
(Croton sebiferum) **JAPANESE TALLOW TREE** (Fig. 33)

DESCRIPTION:

This tree is native to China and flourishes throughout the southern United States. It grows rapidly and reaches a height of about 30 feet. The spike-shaped clusters of yellowish green flowers are followed by terminal clusters of small green "berries". These fruits each contain a 3-lobed capsule that attains a diameter of 1/3 - 1/2 inch. As the fruit matures, it turns blackish-brown and the capsule splits exposing 3 white seeds. The dark green leaves, borne alternately on long slender stems, are rhombic-ovoid in shape, have smooth margins, and are 1 - 3 1/2 inches long and 1 - 3 inches broad, the middle of the leaf being the widest.

GENERAL:

This tree is cultivated widely throughout the state. In many places it has escaped cultivation. The "berries", in both the green and blackish-brown state, are responsible for most of the cases of poisoning, although the leaves are also capable of producing toxicity. Ingestion of the white-hulled seed, once ripe, has not been associated with any symptoms. The toxic principle has not been determined although an oil obtained from this plant has been incriminated (70, 83).

SYMPTOMATOLOGY:

Ingestion of the unripe or maturing berries produces intense gastrointestinal upset with nausea and vomiting occurring fairly rapidly. In studies utilizing domestic animals severe diarrhea, anorexia, generalized weakness, and dehydration were seen. In these animal studies some species showed increased blood urea nitrogen as well as small lesions in the intestinal tract and moderate renal tubular nephritis (70).

TREATMENT:

If vomiting has not already occurred induce emesis and perform gastric lavage. Administer activated charcoal and follow this with a saline cathartic, such as sodium sulfate. Demulcents such as milk, egg white, *et cetera* may be helpful in reducing the gastric irritation. Should vomiting be protracted, dehydration may occur with appropriate fluid and electrolyte therapy being indicated. Treatment thereafter is primarily symptomatic and supportive.

Solanum pseudo-capsicum — JERUSALEM CHERRY, NATAL CHERRY (Fig. 42)

DESCRIPTION:

While this showy shrub can attain a height of 4 feet, it is frequently cultivated as a house pot plant. The bright orange-to-scarlet berries make it a popular Christmas plant. These berries (about 1/2 inch in diameter) are preceded by small white flowers appearing alone or in clusters.

GENERAL:

This entire plant is toxic; the leaves containing the cardioactive substance solanocapsine and the berries containing the glycoalkaloid solanine and related glycoalkaloids. Upon hydrolysis the sugar portion is removed and the alkamine solanidine remains.

When administered experimentally, an intravenous dose of solanocapsine produces a bradycardia (reaching a maximum at about 10 minutes) which persists for about 30 minutes. Atropine pretreatment did not affect the slowing of the heart rate. The compound produces sinus bradycardia, widening of the QRS complex, and lengthening of the P-R and S-T segments (86).

Solanine is not readily absorbed from the gastrointestinal tract, but its saponin-like characteristic makes it highly irritating. Solanidine, presumably more readily absorbed, produces many of the systemic effects, which may or may not be overshadowed by the gastrointestinal effects, depending on their severity (56, 57).

SOLANOCAPSINE

SYMPTOMATOLOGY:

Cardiac depressant effects may result from leaf ingestion, with moderate to severe bradycardia resulting. With ingestion of the berries, symptoms begin to appear only after several hours, and include a harsh, scratchy feeling in both the mouth and pharynx. This is followed by nausea, vomiting, abdominal pain, and diarrhea. A several degree rise in temperature is not uncommon, and therefore this poisoning may be confused with bacterial gastroenteritis. Dizziness, general muscular weakness, pupil dilatation, mental depression, salivation, and sweating may be present. Headache is common and may be related to cerebral edema. Stupefaction and loss of sensation has also been reported. Bloody stools due to intestinal ulceration and hemorrhage, together with proteinuria and hemoglobinuria due to renal involvement, are seen in the later stages of intoxication.

In acute poisoning the systemic symptoms rapidly build to a climax with recovery or death occurring from several hours to 1 - 2 days later. Convulsions may occur, although death is usually associated with falling body temperature, coma, and respiratory paralysis (56, 57, 84).

PATHOLOGY:

Postmortem findings include acute mucosal inflammation of the intestine and stomach. Moderate infiltration and necrosis is seen in the liver (1, 56).

TREATMENT:

If the patient is seen before the gastrointestinal irritation has become apparent, induce emesis and administer activated charcoal. Perform gastric lavage and administer a saline cathartic. Demulcents such as milk, aluminum hydroxide gel, magnesium oxide, or vegetable oil may be administered to help protect the gastrointestinal tract from the intense irritation produced by the glycoalkaloid solanine. Fluid and electrolyte therapy may be necessary if dehydration is present. Thereafter, symptomatic and supportive treatment are indicated.

41

Rheum raponticum — **RHUBARB** (Fig. 43)

DESCRIPTION:
This cultivated garden plant has a large, roughly heart-shaped leaf that reaches up to 1 1/2 feet in length. The red petiole or stalk (stem) is easily recognized and is characteristic of this plant. It is from this stalk that the very tasty rhubarb pie is made.

GENERAL:
The leaf blade (but not the stalk) is quite toxic, particularly if eaten in any quantity. The toxicity of this plant is due to its oxalic acid content, and fatalities have been reported (51, 53, 56, 81). Oxalic acid exerts a corrosive action on the gastrointestinal tract, and once absorbed has a number of actions. The oxalate ion will chelate serum free calcium ion with the formation of insoluble calcium oxalate crystals that precipitate in the renal tubules. Hypocalcemia may occur with potential involvement of the heart, the neuromuscular junction, and the central nervous system.

SYMPTOMATOLOGY:
A lag period of about 24 hours is usually seen after the ingestion of this plant. Following the lag period symptoms include nausea; abdominal pain; and vomiting and diarrhea, both of which may contain blood due to the corrosive nature of oxalic acid. Headache, somnolence, and stupor are a common finding. Electrolyte disturbances, particularly a somewhat refractory hypokalemia, are frequent. Frank tetany seldom occurs, although muscle cramps and twitching of the facial muscles are common. Renal involvement is heralded by oliguria which may proceed to anuria, oxaluria, albuminuria, sometimes hematuria, and elevated serum nonprotein nitrogen levels. The odor of acetone on the patient's breath, as well as a positive test for urinary acetone has been reported (51, 53, 57, 81).

PATHOLOGY:
Calcium oxalate crystals are found in the renal tubules. The kidneys show a histological picture typical of lower nephron nephrosis. The tubules are dilated, their epithelium showing massive degenerative changes. Cloudy swelling, hyaline degeneration, and sclerosis of the tubules is common. Corrosive changes throughout the gastrointestinal tract may be found. Frequently cerebral edema is seen (53, 56).

TREATMENT:
Induce emesis and perform gastric lavage with milk, lime water (calcium hydroxide solution), calcium gluconate or calcium lactate. These solutions will precipitate any free oxalation that is present. Administer activated

charcoal, and if gastrointestinal corrosive effects are not present, administer a saline cathartic such as sodium sulfate. If symptoms of gastroenteritis are already present, administer milk or vegetable oil for their demulcent properties. Intravenous calcium gluconate administration may be necessary. If renal function is adequate, force fluids to prevent urine concentration and calcium oxalate crystal formation. Monitor serum electrolytes closely.

Wild Plants
of the
Woods and/or Meadows

Aesculus arguta — **TEXAS BUCKEYE**

Aesculus pavia — **RED BUCKEYE, FIRECRACKER PLANT** (Fig. 44 a, b, c, d)

DESCRIPTION:

These buckeyes are found as trees or shrubs along the banks of streams or in river bottoms. The red buckeye derives its name from the red flowers it produces, while the Texas buckeye bears yellow flowers. The fruit of these trees is a leathery capsule enclosing 1 - 3 glossy dark brown seeds. Each seed may reach about 1 inch in diameter and bear a large pale scar (hence the name buckeye). Leaves are suspended on a long stalk with 5 - 9 leaflets having serrated margins, the middle of the leaflet being wider than the ends. The buckeyes are found in vegetation areas 1, 2, 3, 4, 5, 7 and 8.

GENERAL:

The leaves, flowers, young sprouts, and seeds of both of these buckeyes are all potentially toxic. Poisoning has occurred in children after they ingested either the nut-like seeds or a "tea" brewed from the young shoots and leaves (44, 78). The principal toxic ingredient of the buckeye is the glycosidic saponin aesculin, which chemically is 6 - beta - glucosido - 7 - hydroxycoumarin. This saponin acts as an irritant in the gastrointestinal tract producing tissue damage and systemic effects if absorbed.

$$C_6H_{11}O_4 \cdot O$$
$$HO$$

AESCULIN

SYMPTOMATOLOGY:

Ingestion of this plant will produce the local irritation associated with saponins resulting in salivation, nausea, vomiting, abdominal pain, and severe diarrhea. Should absorption of the saponin occur, hemolysis to a greater or lesser degree will be seen with subsequent symptoms being proportional to the degree of hemolysis (77). The patient may be quite anxious and complain of headache, fever, and thirst. Facial rash and mydriasis may be present. Muscular weakness, ataxia, and incoordination is seen in the more severe cases. In fatal ingestions mortality was preceded by symptoms of drowsiness, ataxia, facial paralysis, and respiratory paralysis (73).

PATHOLOGY:

Postmortem findings include severe swelling of the intestinal epithelium and lymph follicles. Tissue sloughing may be seen in the stomach, distal ileum, and colon (73).

TREATMENT:

Induce emesis and administer activated charcoal. Perform gastric lavage, and administer demulcents such as milk, vegetable oil, or egg white to help protect the enteric mucosa. Treat for gastroenteritis and administer both fluids and electrolytes to prevent dehydration. Thereafter, treatment is symptomatic and supportive.

Arisaema triphyllum — JACK-IN-THE-PULPIT, INDIAN TURNIP (Fig. 45 a, b)

DESCRIPTION:

This plant is found primarily in moist wooded areas and may reach a height of 3 feet. Usually there are 2 stalks bearing 3 - 5 leaflets (usually 3); each of which may attain 7 inches in length. A central stalk bears the spathe ("flower") which is green in color and striped with purple inside. The fruit of this plant is a cluster of globular red berries (each about 1/2 inch in diameter). The jack-in-the-pulpit is found in vegetation areas 1 and 2.

GENERAL:

The entire plant, and particularly the rhizome and underground tuber, contain needle-like calcium oxalate crystals. If the plant is chewed these crystals penetrate the mucous membranes causing intense irritation, pain, and a burning sensation throughout the oral cavity. Seldom is there an ingestion that does not end with the first mouthful (44, 50, 56, 57).

SYMPTOMATOLOGY:

Biting into any part of this plant produces an immediate burning sensation in the mouth. The intense irritation of the mucous membranes may produce severe edema and swelling of the tongue, lips, palate, and buccal surfaces. Copious salivation and the swollen tongue, along with the accompanying pain and edema, may lead to complete dysphagia or inability to swallow. The swollen state of the tongue and/or pharyngeal edema may physically inhibit respiration.

Any ingestion of the plant may cause severe irritation of the esophagus and stomach, although swallowing does not frequently occur due to the intense burning sensation that is present after the first bite.

PATHOLOGY:

Superficially necrosis of the tongue and buccal mucosa may occur. Irritation and possibly necrosis of the esophagus and stomach may be seen if the plant is swallowed.

TREATMENT:

Therapy includes administering both meperidine for the intense pain and rinsing of the mouth with water and aluminum-magnesium hydroxide suspension. Administration of milk, or aluminum-magnesium hydroxide suspension for their soothing and demulcent effect may be helpful. Be alert for the possibility of performing a tracheostomy should the swollen tongue and throat severely hamper respiration. The edema usually begins to decrease in 2 - 4 days and is essentially gone by 11 - 12 days. The associated pain is quite severe and may not begin to abate for a week or more. Antihistamines may be of some help. In animal experiments with another member of the *Arum* family of plants, cortisone treatment delayed the reaction somewhat, but did not change the total inflammatory response (32).

Podophyllum peltatum — MAYAPPLE, MANDRAKE, GROUND LEMON
(Fig. 46 a, b)

DESCRIPTION:

This 1 or 2-leafed herb has a fleshy rootstock and large, round, umbrella-shaped leaves. The leaves, measuring about 8 inches across are deeply lobed having 3 - 7 irregularly shaped lobes. On flowering plants the solitary, small, white, nodding flower is attached at the fork of the basal stalk between the 2 leaf stems. A solitary ovoid fruit measuring about 2 inches long follows the flower. As the fruit matures, it turns from green to a somewhat irregularly blotched yellow. The mayapple is found in vegetation areas 1, 2 and 3.

GENERAL:

The mayapple contains several resinous compounds. Toxicologically, the most dangerous is podophylloresin which contains up to 20% podophyllotoxin, an antimitotic agent. The rootstock, leaves, stems, and green fruits can cause rather severe poisoning. Mature, yellow fruits are essentially nontoxic and edible, although they may produce mild catharsis. Toxicity due to contact with podophyllum occurs most frequently either among workers during the commercial preparation of podophyllum, or in the treatment of condyloma acuminatum and verrucae vulgares. Its older use in home remedies for its cathartic action also produced a number of intoxications (8, 57).

SYMPTOMATOLOGY:

Ingestion of the leaves, rootstock, or green fruits as well as topical application to mucous membranes, produces severe abdominal pain, persistent vomiting, and severe diarrhea. Respiratory stimulation, vertigo, headache, and elevated body temperature are seen. Lethargy develops later, and convulsive episodes may be seen. Marked elevation in the pulse and respiratory rate, together with hypotension and a severe persistent cough, have been reported (8, 23, 57). Neurologic involvement, persisting several months, has been reported in one case of podophyllum ingestion (20).

TREATMENT:

Treatment is directed toward relieving the severe gastrointestinal irritation and abdominal pain. Chlorpromazine may be given for its antiemetic action. Narcotic analgesics will both help relieve the abdominal pain and suppress the tachypnea. Fluid and electrolyte replacement is necessary to prevent dehydration and shock.

Cicuta maculata — WATER HEMLOCK, SPOTTED COWBANE, POISON PARSNIP (Fig. 47 a, b, c, d, e)

DESCRIPTION:

This perennial herb, reaching 1 - 3 feet in height, is found primarily in damp surroundings particularly along streams and in marshy areas. It has small white flowers which form umbrella-shaped or flat-top clusters similar to those of the closely related poison hemlock *(Conium maculatum).* The narrow leaflets attain 1 - 4 inches in length and have serrated margins. The leaflets from the top of the plant vary considerably from those nearer the base, the latter being broader. The major veins of each leaflet terminate in the notch of the serration as opposed to the tip of the serration. The fruit of this plant is a small, two-part capsule which contains many seeds. Several tuberous roots, which are thicker toward their centers, make up the major root system. If the thickened base of the stem is cut lengthwise through the root, several thin chambers separated by cross partitions are seen. From the cut surfaces a yellow oily liquid will ooze out smelling much like fresh parsnip. The water hemlock is found in vegetation areas 1, 2, 3, 4, 7 and 8.

GENERAL:

The root of this plant has been mistaken for ginseng, a medicinal Chinese root, with a fatality resulting (16). It is not uncommon for this plant to be fatally mistaken for a "wild carrot". Drying does not appreciably reduce the toxicity. The plant contains a highly toxic substance known as cicutoxin. The root and rootstock contain the highest concentration, but the entire

50

plant may contain some of this toxic substance, particularly in the early stages of growth (63). Cicutoxin is a potent convulsant. Symptoms begin 15 minutes to 1 hour after ingestion. A portion of the plant as small as 3/8 inch in diameter may produce fatal poisoning (32).

$$HOCH_2 (CH_2)_2 - (C \equiv C)_2 - (CH = CH)_3 - \overset{\overset{\displaystyle OH}{|}}{C}HCH_2 CH_2 CH_3$$

CICUTOXIN

SYMPTOMATOLOGY:

Shortly after ingestion of the plant salivation, abdominal pain, nausea, and vomiting are seen. Tremors and muscle spasms are followed rapidly by convulsions which culminate in exhaustion, respiratory failure, circulatory collapse, and death. Some species of *Cicuta* produce severe hypotension (67).

TREATMENT:

If vomiting has not already occurred, induce emesis and administer activated charcoal. Perform gastric lavage and follow this with a saline cathartic (*i.e.,* sodium sulfate). If convulsions have already appeared, the use of short-acting barbiturates and parenteral phenobarbital are indicated. The cause of death partially· depends on the length of the acute phase of the intoxication. Support respiration and treat symptomatically and supportively. Usually if the patient survives the acute phase he recovers with few after-effects.

Karwinskia humboldtiana — **COYOTILLO, TULLIDORA, WILD CHERRY** (Fig. 48 a, b, c, d)

DESCRIPTION:

This plant appears as a shrub or small tree, that can attain a height of about 6 - 8 feet. Flowers are borne as clusters and are small and greenish in color. Leaves (3/4 to 2 inches long and 1/2 to 1 inch wide) are a dark lustrous green above and and paler below. The underside of the leaf may show black spots and is prominently veined. The small, reddish-brown to black "berries" (1/4 to 3/8 inch) mature in mid-autumn. The coyotillo is found in vegetation areas 2, 6, 7 and 10.

GENERAL:

Both the leaves and the "berries" of this plant are toxic and have caused both fatalities in livestock and poisoning in children. The toxic principle has been as yet only partially characterized (55). After ingestion of the berries, there is a lag period of several days or even weeks before the first symptoms of poisoning are seen. Once symptoms begin, the clinical picture is one of progressive and symmetrical polyneuropathy, the lower limbs being initially affected. Later effects include both respiratory and bulbar paralysis (14.)

Experimental studies have shown that in motor nerves there is swelling of Schwann cells, myelin sheath clefts, segmental demyelination, and Wallerian degeneration. Although nerve injury was seen in both long and short motor nerves, the damage was greatest at more distal sites in the long motor nerves (18). High doses of the "berries" of this plant produced central nervous system lesions as well. Swellings along the axons of Purkinje cells in the cerebellum as well as in the white matter of the spinal cord were noted (19). Widespread skeletal and myocardial muscle degeneration has also been experimentally produced (28).

SYMPTOMATOLOGY:

The symptoms of polyneuropathy will manifest themselves as frequent stumbling and falling, which progresses to an inability to walk or crawl. The upper limbs will also become affected, as will the intercostal muscles. The patient becomes quadraplegic and suffers from respiratory insufficiency. There usually is no sensory deficit. A slight elevation in serum glutamic oxalacetic transaminase (SGOT) may be present (14).

TREATMENT:

If the patient is seen soon after ingesting the coyotillo berries, induce emesis, perform gastric lavage, and administer activated charcoal. Follow this with the administration of a saline cathartic. After the onset of the polyneuropathy symptoms, the treatment is basically symptomatic and supportive. Hospitalization of several months duration may be necessary, although nearly complete recovery is the rule. The patient may remain areflexic for some time after he has regained the ability to stand and walk (14).

Parthenocissus quinquefolia — **VIRGINIA CREEPER, AMERICAN IVY**
(Psedera quinquefolia) (Fig. 49 a, b, c)

DESCRIPTION:

This climbing vine attaches itself to walls, trees, *et cetera,* by means of adhesive discs which are attached to its multibranched vine. The leaves are typically divided into 5 coarsely toothed leaflets that are attached to the vine by a stalk which may vary from 3 inches to 1 foot in length. Leaflets may vary from 2 to 6 inches long. Small (2 - 6 mm.) greenish-blue to black berries mature in the fall of the year. The Virginia creeper is found in vegetation areas 1, 2, 3, 4, 5, 6, 7 and 8.

GENERAL:

The berry is the portion usually involved in poisoning, although the leaf is most probably toxic as well. The toxicity of this plant is due to its oxalic acid content. Fatalities due to its ingestion have been reported (57). Oxalic acid exerts a corrosive action on the gastrointestinal tract and once absorbed has a number of actions. Oxalate ion will chelate serum free calcium ion with the formation of an insoluble calcium oxalate crystal which precipitates in the renal tubules. Hypocalcemia may occur with potential involvement of the heart, the neuromuscular junction, and the central nervous system.

SYMPTOMATOLOGY:

A lag period of about 24 hours is usually seen after the ingestion of this plant. Following the lag period, symptoms include nausea, abdominal pain, and vomiting and diarrhea (both of which may contain blood due to the corrosive nature of oxalic acid). Headache, somnolence, and stupor are a common finding. Electrolyte disturbances, particularly a somewhat refractory hypokalemia, are frequent. Frank tetany seldom occurs, although muscle cramps and twitching of the facial muscles are common. Renal involvement is heralded by oliguria which may proceed to anuria, oxaluria, albuminuria, sometimes hematuria, and elevated serum nonprotein nitrogen levels. The odor of acetone on the patient's breath as well as a positive test for urinary acetone have been reported (57).

PATHOLOGY:

Calcium oxalate crystals are found in the renal tubules. The kidneys show a histological picture typical of lower nephron nephrosis. The tubules are dilated, their epithelium showing massive degenerative changes. Cloudy swelling, hyaline degeneration, and sclerosis of the tubules are common. Corrosive changes throughout the gastrointestinal tract may be found. Frequently, cerebral edema is seen (56).

TREATMENT:

Induce emesis and perform gastric lavage with milk, lime water (calcium hydroxide solution), calcium gluconate or calcium lactate. These solutions will precipitate any free oxalate ion that is present. Administer activated charcoal, and if gastrointestinal corrosive effects are not present, administer milk or vegetable oil for their demulcent properties. Intravenous calcium gluconate administration may be necessary. If renal function is adequate, force fluids to prevent urine concentration and calcium oxalate crystal formation. Monitor serum electrolytes closely.

Conium maculatum — **POISON HEMLOCK, FOOL'S PARSLEY, FALSE PARSLEY** (Fig. 51, a, b, c, d, e)

DESCRIPTION:

This erect plant grows to a height of 4 - 6 feet. The stems are stout, green, hollow except at the nodes, and usually spotted with purple, particularly in the lower portions. The umbrella-like clusters of small, white flowers appear at the end of the larger stems and are supported by numerous smaller stems. The leaves are lacy and are triangular in outline. It is a biennial plant having a two-year growing cycle, producing fruits only in the second year. The small fruits are grayish-brown and have conspicuous wavy ridges. Each plant has a single white tap root. The poison hemlock is found in vegetation areas 2, 4, 7 and 10.

GENERAL:

The poison hemlock is of some historical importance since it was this plant that was used to poison Socrates (26). The entire plant is poisonous, the most toxic parts being the leaves in the fall of the first year. In the second growing year the leaves, flowers, and fruits of the plant are all toxic (25). Three alkaloids make up the principle toxic components. These are lambda-coniceine, coniine, and N-methylconiine. The experimentally determined oral LD 50's in mice (producing death within 12 minutes) are 12 mg/Kg, 100 mg/Kg, and 204 mg/Kg, respectively (11).

CONIINE

These alkaloids have a number of pharmacological actions resembling nicotine in many respects. They produce stimulation and then depression of all autonomic ganglia, thus an initial hypertensive effect, followed by hypotension may be seen. Their action includes a slight depolarizing effect on the myoneural junction. There is evidence that this myoneuro-blocking action is due to an intracellular mechanism which renders the endplate inexcitable by acetylcholine. These alkaloids also have a central depressant activity (11).

SYMPTOMATOLOGY:

Symptoms of poisoning usually appear fairly rapidly after ingestion of the plant. These symptoms include: gastrointestinal distress with nausea and vomiting, muscular weakness, convulsions, and respiratory distress. Trembling, ataxia, dilated pupils, and weakened heartbeat may also be present. Death occurs due to the gradually increasing muscular weakness and/or convulsions followed by paralysis and respiratory failure (44, 56).

PATHOLOGY:

Postmortem examination reveals a considerable gastrointestinal inflammation and widespread congestion.

TREATMENT:

Rapidly induce emesis if vomiting has not already begun. Perform gastric lavage with 1:5,000 potassium permanganate and large amounts of water. Administer activated charcoal. Symptomatic and supportive therapy includes supporting respiration and treatment of any seizure activity.

Momordica balsamina
Momordica charantia — **WILD BALSAM-APPLE, BALSAM PEAR, BITTER GOURD** (Fig. 50)

DESCRIPTION:

Both species of this plant are quite similar in appearance. They are creeping or climbing vines with deeply lobed leaves. The small flowers are yellow and tubular-shaped. Small warty projections cover the fruits which turn yellow or orange as they mature. These ovoid fruits vary from 1 1/2 - 5 inches long and taper to a point at each end. At maturity, the yellow fruit splits exposing 15 - 20 seeds that have a bright red fleshy covering (aril). These plants are found along the Gulf coast in sandy soils and waste areas. The wild balsam-apple is found in vegetation area 2.

GENERAL:

The seeds, leaves, and the yellow body of the mature fruit contain highly irritant saponins. In some species the red fleshy aril is nonpoisonous. Saponins, in general produce severe irritation of the gastrointestinal tract and may cause deep tissue damage due to their corrosive nature. Once absorbed into the bloodstream they are quite hemolytic (44, 56, 57).

SYMPTOMATOLOGY:

Ingestion of small amounts of this plant will produce the local irritation associated with saponins resulting in salivation, nausea, vomiting, abdominal pain, and severe diarrhea. Should absorption of the saponin occur, hemolysis, to a greater or lesser degree, will be seen with the symptoms being proportional to the amount of hemolysis (77). The patient may complain of headache, fever, thirst, and may be quite anxious. Facial rash and mydriasis may be present. Muscular weakness, ataxia, and incoordination may be present in the more serious cases.

TREATMENT:
    Induce emesis and administer activated charcoal. Perform both gastric lavage and administer demulcents such as milk, vegetable oil, or egg white to help protect the enteric mucosa. Treat for gastroenteritis and administer fluids and electrolytes to prevent dehydration. Thereafter, treatment is symptomatic and supportive.

Sophora secundiflora — **MESCAL BEAN, TEXAS MOUNTAIN-LAUREL**
(Fig. 52 a, b)

DESCRIPTION:
    This evergreen shrub or tree can attain a height of 35 feet. The leaves consist of 5 - 13 elliptical-to-oblong leaflets each ranging from 1 - 2 1/2 inches long and 1/2 - 1 1/2 inches wide. These leathery, dark green leaflets are lustrous on the upper surface and paler on the underside. The flowers consist of terminal pale lavender clusters that are strongly fragrant. A leathery seed pod, 1 - 5 inches long, is produced and usually contains 3 - 4 seeds that are bright red when mature. The mescal bean is found in vegetation areas 2, 4, 6, 7 and 10.

GENERAL:
    The entire plant contains the toxic substance cytisine, an alkaloid that has a nicotine-like action. Toxicity of the individual parts of this plant increases as they mature. The seeds were used by the indians for their reputed narcotic properties (83). A hard seed coat protects the seed from digestion and if they are swallowed without first being broken they usually pass through the gastrointestinal tract intact. If cracked or broken, ingestion of the seed may produce severe symptoms of toxicity. One seed, throughly chewed, has been considered the lethal dose (56). The active principle, cytisine, is rapidly absorbed through the oral cavity, mucous membranes, and the gastrointestinal tract and is rapidly excreted, primarily *via* the kidneys (57).

CYTISINE

56

SYMPTOMATOLOGY:

Symptoms usually develop within about 1 hour and include mucous membrane irritation, manifested by increased salivation. Nausea and violent, sometimes bloody, vomiting occurs and may continue for some time. Abdominal pain and diarrhea are usually absent or very minimal. Headache, vertigo, confusion, excessive thirst, and a cold sweat may be present. Increased body temperature and mydriasis may be present. Muscle fasciculation, convulsions, depressed or absent spinal reflexes, paralysis, and coma have been reported (44, 57). Initial respiratory stimulation is followed by progressively weaker respiration and Cheyne-Stokes type breathing may occur with death due to respiratory failure (44).

TREATMENT:

If vomiting has not already occurred spontaneously, induce emesis and perform gastric lavage. Administer activated charcoal and a saline cathartic. Support respiration and be prepared to manage any seizure activity. Hypotension may occur and pressor agents may be necessary to maintain the blood pressure. Oliguria and anuria may occur and require appropriate therapy. Thereafter, treatment is supportive and symptomatic.

Phoradendron serotinum — **MISTLETOE, AMERICAN MISTLETOE,**
(P. flavescens) **CHRISTMAS MISTLETOE** (Fig. 54)

DESCRIPTION:

This favorite Christmas ornamental is a semi-parasitic shrub growing on deciduous trees. Its leaves and branches are yellowish-green to dark green in color. The leaves, 1 - 2 inches long and 1/2 to 1 inch wide, have smooth margins and a leathery texture. Small (about 3/16 inch), white, one-seeded berries are produced. The mistletoe is found in vegetation areas 1, 3, 4 and 5.

GENERAL:

All parts of the mistletoe contain the toxic principles beta-phenethylamine and tyramine. The berries are the portions most frequently involved in poisoning. Death has occurred in about 12 hours after the ingestion of a "tea" brewed from the berries of this plant (61). The toxic substances have a direct stimulatory action on smooth muscle, as well as an indirect action via the adrenergic nervous system. Thus there is stimulation of the vasculature, intestines, urinary bladder, and the uterus in females. This latter activity has lead to the use of mistletoe as an abortifacient, oftentimes with deleterious effects (61).

SYMPTOMATOLOGY:
Symptoms of acute ingestion of mistletoe leaves and berries incorporate signs of acute gastroenteritis including nausea, vomiting, and diarrhea. Abdominal pain may also be present. Further symptoms may include tachypnea, which may be followed by dyspnea, hypertension, delerium, and possibly hallucinations. Mydriasis, sweating, convulsions, and cardiovascular collapse have also been reported. The severe dehydration that may follow profuse vomiting and diarrhea may produce either shock or a shock-like syndrome (61).

TREATMENT:
If the symptoms of gastroenteritis are not already present, induce emesis and perform gastric lavage. Administer activated charcoal and a saline cathartic such as sodium sulfate. Watch for initial hypertension followed by hypotension, shock, and possible cardiovascular collapse. Appropriate parenteral fluid and electrolyte therapy is indicated if dehydration is present (35).

Solanum americanum — **BLACK NIGHTSHADE, DEADLY NIGHTSHADE, COMMON NIGHTSHADE, AMERICAN NIGHTSHADE** (Fig. 56 a, b)

Solanum carolinense — **CAROLINA HORSENETTLE, HORSE NETTLE** (Fig. 53 a, b)

Solanum eleagnifolium— **SILVERLEAF NIGHTSHADE, DEVIL'S TOMATO** (Fig. 55 a, b)

DESCRIPTION:
Solanum americanum - **BLACK NIGHTSHADE** - This annual plant, which is found throughout the state, grows to a height of 2 - 3 feet or may spread along the ground. It has small white flowers which may be found on the same plant along with the green and/or mature black berries. The black nightshade is found in vegetation areas 1, 2, 3, 4, 5, 6, 7, 8, 9 and 10.

Solanum carolinense - **CAROLINA HORSENETTLE** - The stems and leaf veins of this perennial weed are covered with numerous sharp yellowish spines. The leaves are dark green above and paler beneath. Pale violet or white flowers are followed by green berries which turn bright yellow as they mature. The Carolina horsenettle is found in vegetation areas 1, 2, 3, 4 and 7.

58

Solanum eleagnifolium - **SILVERLEAF NIGHTSHADE** - This perennial weed attains a height of 1 - 3 feet. The leaves and stems have a white-to-silver hairy appearance. The stems and leaf ribs usually bear short sharp spines. The blue-to-violet flowers are followed by berries that turn from green, to yellow, to black as they mature. The silverleaf nightshade is found in vegetation areas 1, 2, 3, 4, 5, 6, 7, 8, 9 and 10.

GENERAL:

All parts of these plants are toxic, although poisoning is usually associated with the ingestion of the berries. In the immature green state the berries are quite poisonous, but decrease in toxicity as they mature.

The toxicity of these plants is due to the presence of the glycoalkaloid solanine and related compounds. With hydrolysis, the sugar portion is split off and the alkamine solanidine is produced. The unhydrolyzed solanine is not readily absorbed from the gastrointestinal tract, but its saponin-like character makes it highly irritating. The alkamine (solanidine), which presumably is more readily absorbed, has systemic effects which may be overshadowed if the gastrointestinal effects are severe (56, 57).

SOLANINE   SOLANIDINE

SYMPTOMATOLOGY:

Symptoms appear several hours after ingestion and initially include a harsh, scratchy sensation in the mouth and pharynx. This is followed by nausea, vomiting, abdominal pain, and diarrhea. A several degree rise in temperature is not uncommon; thus poisoning may be confused with bacterial gastroenteritis. Dizziness, general muscular weakness, pupil dilatation, mental depression, salivation, and sweating may be present. Headache is common, and may be related to cerebral edema. Restless movement of the arms and head, as well as stupefaction and loss of sensation, have also been reported. Bloody stools (due to intestinal ulceration and hemorrhage), together with proteinuria and hemglobinuria are seen in the later stages of intoxication.

59

In acute poisoning the systemic symptoms rapidly build to a climax with recovery or death occuring in either several hours or 1 - 2 days later. Convulsions may occur, although death is usually associated with falling body temperature, coma, and respiratory paralysis (56, 57, 84).

PATHOLOGY:
Postmortem findings include acute mucosal inflammation of the intestine and stomach. Moderate fatty infiltration and necrosis is seen in the liver (56, 84).

TREATMENT:
If the patient is seen before the gastrointestinal irritation has become apparent, induce emesis and administer activated charcoal. Perform gastric lavage and administer a saline cathartic. Demulcents such as milk, aluminum hydroxide gel, magnesium oxide, or vegetable oil may be administered to help protect the gastrointestinal tract from the intense irritation produced by the glycoalkaloid solanine. Dehydration may occur rapidly and requires appropriate fluid and electrolyte therapy. Thereafter, symptomatic and supportive treatment are indicated.

Sesbania drummondii *(Daubentonia longifolia)*	—	**SENNA-BEAN, RATTLEBOX, COFFEE-BEAN, SENNIE-BEAN, RATTLEBUSH** (Fig. 57 a, b)
Sesbania punicea *(Daubentonia punicea)*	—	**PURPLE RATTLEBOX, DAUBENTONIA, BRAZIL RATTLEBOX** (Fig. 58 a, b)
Sesbania vesicarium *(Glottidium vesicarium)*	—	**BAGPOD, BLADDERPOD, COFFEEBEAN** (Fig. 59 a, b)

DESCRIPTION:
Sesbania drummondii - **SENNA-BEAN** - This plant may appear as a shrub or as a small tree which sometimes reaches 20 feet in height. It is a perennial which grows primarily in low, wet areas. The golden-yellow flowers are borne in racemes (long clusters, 2 to 6 inches). A seed pod that is 4-sided with 4 wings running the length of the pod is often found on the bare tree during the fall and winter. The seed pod turns from green, to yellow, to dark brown as it matures. The pod will contain 4 to 7 small, hard seeds. The leaves, 5 to 8 inches long, are made up of 12 to 60 small green leaflets (3/8 to 1 inch long). Leaflets are arranged in pairs, each being opposite the other on a central stem. The senna-bean is found in vegetation areas 1, 2, 3, 4 and 6.

Sesbania punicea - **PURPLE RATTLEBOX** - This perennial plant appears as an open shrub reaching 10 feet in height. The flowers are borne in 2 1/2 to 5 inch racemes (long clusters) and may be from red-orange to purple in color. The leaves (3 1/2 - 6 inches long) are alternately arranged on the stem and are made up of 6 to 20 pairs of green leaflets one inch or less in length. A fruit consisting of a 4-sided, 4-winged (running lengthwise) seed pod, containing varying numbers of seeds, is produced in mid-summer. Frequently, the dried pods can be found on the tree throughout the winter. The purple rattlebox is found in vegetation areas 1, 2 and 3.

Sesbania vesicaria - **BAGPOD** - This annual, widely branched, herbacious plant may attain a height of 12 feet. The flowers, appearing in late summer, are borne in clusters of 2 - 5 flowers on slender 3 - 5 inch stalks. They range in color from yellow, striped with pink, to solid red (depending on the particular variety). The dull green, alternately arranged leaves (5 - 9 inches long), are made up of 10 to 27 oppositely arranged leaflet pairs (1/2 - 1 inch long). A legume-like seed pod containing 1 or 2 seeds is produced. The dried walls of the seed pod are made of a thin, white, papery membrane, hence the name "bladderpod" or bagpod". The bagpod is found in vegetation areas 1, 2, 3, 4, 5 and 6.

GENERAL:

Saponins have been detected in both the bagpod and purple rattlebox, and are presumably present in the senna-bean as well. The symptoms produced by ingestion and the pathology seen is essentially the same with all three of these plants (56). Numerous livestock have been killed by these plants. One fatality of a small boy occurred after ingestion of the seeds of the senna-bean *(Sesbania drummondii)*. The entire plant can produce toxicity, although there appears to be an increased concentration of the saponins in the seeds.

SYMPTOMATOLOGY:

After ingestion of these plants, either relatively rapid induction of vomiting may occur or the patient may be asymptomatic for up to 24 hours. The irritating and corrosive nature of the saponins is manifested as anorexia, nausea, repeated vomiting, abdominal pain, and diarrhea, all signs of the severe gastroenteritis which is produced. Should absorption of the saponin occur, hemolysis to a greater or lesser degree will be seen with subsequent symptoms being proportional to the amount of hemolysis (77). Depression, muscular weakness, and prostration may be seen. Shallow and rapid respiration, together with a fast, irregular pulse has also been reported (56).

PATHOLOGY:

Postmortem examination reveals either small thrombi of degenerated red blood cells throughout the circulatory system or the presence of dark, tarry blood. Degenerative changes are seen in the lymphatics and in the smooth musculature. Severe hemorrhagic inflammation of the gastrointestinal tract with considerable tissue sloughing is seen. Histologically, there is generalized congestion and albuminous degeneration in the kidneys and liver. Some hepatic necrosis may also be observed (56).

TREATMENT:

If the immediate signs of gastric irritation has not produced spontaneous vomiting, emesis should be induced. Perform gastric lavage and administer activated charcoal. A saline cathartic (such as sodium sulfate) should be administered if the signs of gastroenteritis are not present. If gastrointestinal irritation is apparent, demulcents such as milk, egg white, vegetable oil, *et cetera,* should be administered for their soothing and protective effect. Severe dehydration has been known to occur and must be guarded against. Appropriate fluid and electrolyte therapy is indicated should dehydration be already present. Treatment thereafter is symptomatic and supportive.

Lophophora williamsii — **PEYOTE, MESCAL BUTTON, MESCAL** (Fig. 61)

DESCRIPTION:

Peyote is a small (1 - 3 inches in diameter) cactus which bears no spines and is hemispherical in shape. The top of the cactus has small rounded sections which bear tufts of yellowish hair. A small white-to-pink flower is produced from the center of the top. A ripe pink berry containing black seeds is also produced. Peyote is found in vegetation areas 6, 7 and 10.

GENERAL:

The peyote cactus contains about 6% of the alkaloid mescaline as well as other related alkaloids. Poisoning results from the chewing of the fresh or dried aboveground plants ("buttons"). The taste is quite disagreeable and very bitter. If vomiting does not intervene, the psychedelic effect of mescaline hallucinations, primarily of a visual nature, will be seen (44, 54).

MESCALINE

62

SYMPTOMATOLOGY:

Nausea and vomiting frequently occur after the ingestion of the green or dry "button". The pharmacological effects of mescaline include anxiety, sympathomimetic stimulation, limb hyperreflexia, and tremors. Hallucinations, particularly those that are visual in nature (brightly colored lights and colors), and space distortions may occur. With these exceptions, the sensorium is relatively normal and insight is retained. Large doses of mescaline can produce symptoms for up to 12 hours (42, 54).

TREATMENT:

If the psychedelic symptoms have not begun, induce emesis and perform gastric lavage. Administer activated charcoal and a saline cathartic such as sodium sulfate. Psychiatric care may be indicated. Parenteral chlorpromazine may be administered to antagonize many of the effects of the mescaline.

Datura meteloides — **MOONFLOWER, ANGEL'S TRUMPET, HAIRY THORNAPPLE, LOCOWEED** (Fig. 62 a, b, c, d)

Datura stramonium — **JIMSONWEED, JAMESTOWN WEED, THORN APPLE, ANGEL'S TRUMPET** (Fig. 63)

DESCRIPTION:

Datura meteloides - **MOONFLOWER** - This *Datura* attains 1 - 3 feet in height and has large (to 9 inches), white, trumpet or funnel-shaped flowers that open only during the evening hours. This plant is peculiar in that the entire plant is covered with fine plant hairs which gives the surface a grayish velvet-like appearance. The fruits are spherical and are covered with long slender spines which may be up to 2 inches in length. This species is frequently found in gardens as a cultivated ornamental. The moonflower is found growing wild in vegetation areas 6, 7 and 10.

Datura stramonium - **JIMSONWEED** - This stout, erect, annual herb is found as a weed, primarily in waste areas, and can attain a height of 3 - 5 feet. It has large (3 - 8 inches long), short-stalked leaves with irregular large teeth on the leaf margin. The flowers are white, relatively large, and trumpet-shaped, usually about 4 inches long. Hard, sharp spines cover the ovoid capsule of the fruit. As the fruit matures and dries, the capsule splits from the end into four pieces exposing many small (3 - 4 mm.) seeds. The jimsonweed is found in vegetation areas 1, 2, 3, 5, 7, 8, 9 and 10.

63

GENERAL:
   Both of these species contain considerable quantities of the tropane or belladonna alkaloids throughout the entire plant. The leaves of *Datura stramonium* contain from 0.2 - 0.45% of the belladonna alkaloids, with atropine, hyoscyamine, and scopolamine predominating (79). The seeds of this plant contains about 0.4% alkaloids consisting principally of hyoscyamine (21). *Datura meteloides* contains up to 0.1% scopolamine as well as considerable amounts of atropine, hyoscyamine, and related alkaloids. The seeds of these plants are commonly involved in poisoning (21, 79). Children are attracted to the large white flowers and poisoning has resulted by their sucking the nectar from the flowers (58). Secondary poisonings have occurred due to the eating of honey made from the nectar of these and other *Datura* species. Handling the leaves followed by rubbing the eyes has been known to produce mydriasis. Calculation of the approximate fatal dose of pure atropine in children puts the lethal dose of seeds or leaves of these plants at 4 - 5 Gm. (69), although death has been reported in a 2-year-old child after the ingestion of 100 seeds (total weight just over 1 Gm.) (76).

SYMPTOMATOLOGY:
   The symptoms of poisoning depend somewhat on the species of *Datura* involved. The amount of material ingested, as well as the relative concentrations of the alkaloids present will determine in large measure the sequence and severity of symptoms seen with poisoning. The usual symptoms that are seen are those of typical atropine intoxication, classically described as "hot as a hare, blind as a bat, dry as a bone, red as a beet, and mad as a wet hen" (88). If the scopolamine content of the plant is relatively high, these symptoms are somewhat confused due to the fact that scopolamine does not produce nearly as much peripheral vasodilation or temperature rise as does atropine. Also, there is relatively little increase in the heart rate and only a short period of cerebral excitation with high scopolamine concentrations (42).
   Symptoms include: widely dilated pupils which respond only sluggishly to light, dry mouth, elevated body temperature, and intense thirst. A hot, dry, flushed skin may be present, as well as an erythematous rash, particularly on the chest, neck, and face. Confusion, weakness, marked ataxia, and nonpurposeful thrashing movement may appear. The CNS effects of these alkaloids may be manifest as delerium, mania, hallucinations (both visual and auditory), and psychotic behavior. The pulse will be rapid and weak. There may also be constipation and urinary retention (59).

TREATMENT:
   Induce emesis and administer activated charcoal. Perform gastric lavage using 1:5000 potassium permanganate and large volumes of water. Follow

this with more activated charcoal and a saline cathartic (*i.e.* sodium sulfate). Most cholinergic drugs can reduce somewhat the degree of parasympathetic blockade, but have less effect on the central effects of the alkaloids. Physostigmine, a cholinesterase inhibitor, is the drug of choice in these cases since it penetrates the blood-brain barrier, as opposed to neostigmine which does not, thus providing central as well as peripheral antagonism. Since physostigmine is rapidly destroyed, its parenteral administration (adults: 1 - 2 mg slowly IV) may have to be repeated in 1 - 2 hours (42). A short-acting barbiturate may be considered should the central excitatory effects become severe. External cooling of the patient with cold baths may help to reduce the body temperature. The ophthalmic administration of pilocarpine (1% solution) together with the use of a darkened room may help reduce eye discomfort. Cooling drinks may help to relieve the dryness of the mouth and throat.

Robinia pseudoacacia — **BLACK LOCUST, WHITE LOCUST**
(Fig. 64 a, b, c, d, e)

DESCRIPTION:
   This tree attains heights of 80 - 100 feet and has numerous sharp spines which are usually located at the base of the leaf stalks. The 8 - 14 inch leaf consists of 7 - 19 oppositely arranged leaflets each measuring up to 2 inches long and 1 inch wide. White racemes (clusters) of flowers appear in late spring and are followed by brown flattened beans, each containing 4 - 8 hard flattened seeds. The black locust is found in vegetation areas 1, 2, 3, 4, 5 and 9.

GENERAL:
   Poisoning due to ingestion of the young leaves, inner bark, and seeds has been reported (44, 56). The flowers do not appear to be toxic (57). The toxins have been identified and partially characterized as robin, a heat-labile toxalbumin, and robitin, a glycoside (56). Fatalities due to ingestion of this plant are rare.

SYMPTOMATOLOGY:
   Ingestion of the black locust initially produces nausea, vomiting, and epigastric pain after a lag period of about 1 hour. The vomitus may be bloody and contain mucus. A flushed face, dry mouth, and mydriasis may be present. More severe poisoning may produce a feeble pulse, cool extremities, and stupor. Respiration may be irregular. Convulsions may occur and muscle fasiculations have been observed (36, 44).

65

TREATMENT:

No specific antidote is known to counteract the poisoning that this plant produces. The gastrointestinal symptoms may be treated with demulcents and protectives such as milk, bismuth subcarbonate, or magnesium trisilicate. Meperidine may be indicated for relief of the epigastric pain. If the patient is discovered prior to the onset of GI symptoms, emesis should be induced followed by gastric lavage. A saline cathartic such as sodium sulfate should be administered. The shock-like symptoms that occur in the latter phases of the poisoning may be guarded against by the use of intravenous fluids. Recovery is usually complete within 24 - 48 hours and may only require short term hospitalization if the symptoms so dictate.

Lobelia cardinalis   —   **CARDINAL FLOWER** (Fig. 67)

Nicotiana glauca   —   **TREE TOBACCO** (Fig. 65 a, b)

DESCRIPTION:

Lobelia cardinalis - **CARDINAL FLOWER** - This perennial plant reaches 5 feet or more in height. Numerous thin, irregularly serrated leaves are produced and range from 40 to 20 inches in length. Deep red flowers (1 to 2 inches long) are borne on the central stalk as well as on secondary stems. It grows wild primarily along river banks and damp ground, although it is frequently cultivated for its showy red blooms. The cardinal flower is found in vegetation areas 1, 2, 3 and 4.

Nicotiana glauca - **TREE TOBACCO** - This perennial evergreen shrub or small tree may attain a height of 20 feet. The trunk is slender and the branches are flexible, slender, and green. Eliptical leaves, 2 to 6 inches or more in length, are borne on long stems. The leaves are light green to grayish-green, slightly leathery, and are covered with a thin, waxy coating. Yellow tubular flowers appear in clusters, with the individual flowers measuring 1 to 2 inches. The fruit of the plant is an egg-shaped seed pod about 1/2 inch long. This shrub is commonly found in waste areas. The tree tobacco is found in vegetation areas 2, 6, 7 and 10.

GENERAL:

The cardinal flower owes its toxicity to its relatively high concentration (from 0.13 to 0.63%) of the alkaloid lobeline and other related alkaloids. The pharmacology and toxicology of these alkaloids are similar to that of nicotine, which, along with the closely related alkaloid anabasine, is responsible for the toxicity of the tree tobacco (*N. glauca*) (42, 55, 64).

Nicotine and lobeline both produce initial stimulation and then depression of autonomic ganglia. Stimulation of medullary centers including the emetic and respiratory centers is followed by subsequent depression of the centers. Myoneural junction stimulation and depression may be seen, although the rapidly developing paralysis usually obscures the stimulant effect.

LOBELINE   NICOTINE   ANABASINE

SYMPTOMATOLOGY:

Symptoms of intoxication include nausea, salivation, abdominal pain, and vomiting. Severe diarrhea, sweating, headache, dizziness, marked weakness, and disturbed vision and hearing may be present. Respiration may be initially stimulated and then depressed. Hypertension and miosis may be seen during the early stages of intoxication. As the symptoms progress, hypotension will ensue, the pupils will dilate and the pulse will be rapid and thready (42, 64).

TREATMENT:

Usually the initial vomiting, which occurs fairly rapidly after ingestion, will help to empty the stomach. If no vomiting has occurred, induce emesis and perform gastric lavage. Administer large amounts of activated charcoal and follow with a saline cathartic (*i.e.,* sodium sulfate). Support respiration and watch for possible cardiac arrhythmias. Guard against dehydration with appropriate fluid and electrolyte therapy. Death, if it occurs, is usually due to paralysis of the respiratory muscles.

Phytolacca americana —   **POKEWEED, POKEROOT, POKE SALAD, INKBERRY** (Fig. 68 a, b)

DESCRIPTION:

This native perennial herb has a stout stalk and can attain 6 to 9 feet in height. It has a large root measuring from 4 to 6 inches in diameter. The leaves are smooth margined, can attain 4 to 6 inches in length, and are arranged alternately on the stem. The plant has a strong, rather unpleasant odor. Numerous small, white or slightly green flowers appear, followed by long racemes of berries. The berries are attached by a short stem to a long stalk. As they mature, the berries turn from green to a very dark purple. The pokeweed is found in vegetation areas 1, 2, 3, 4, 5, 6, 7 and 8.

67

GENERAL:

The entire plant is poisonous, particularly the root, leaves and green berries. The mature berries have been used in making pies, although the raw berries may have been responsible for a human fatality (56). The root has produced serious intoxications after it was mistaken for horseradish or parsnips (38). When the leaf is cooked properly it is edible, but if it is either ingested raw or improperly prepared it also can produce toxic manifestations. Parboiling the leaf, with disposal of the first and last cooking water, is necessary in order to render the leaves nontoxic. The toxic principles of the pokeweed have not been fully characterized, although it is known that there is tannin and a resin present throughout the plant (79). Presumably, these substances are responsible for the symptoms seen after ingestion of the root or uncooked leaves (57). Experimentally, this plant or a crude extract of it produces direct stimulation of the gastrointestinal tract that cannot be overcome even with the use of ganglionic blocking agents (65).

Another interesting feature of this plant is the fact that in children who have either ingested the berries or had open wounds come into contact with the berry juice, an increase in the number of mitotic cells in the peripheral blood has been observed. In each instance studied, large cells which are morphologically typical of plasmablasts and proplasmacytes as well as plasma cells are seen for up to 2 weeks after exposure. In the peripheral blood smears studied, this spectrum of "plasmacytoid lymphocytes" accounted for from 0.4 to 10.8% of the lymphocytes counted. No definite clinical features were observed that were associated with the peripheral blood changes (9).

SYMPTOMATOLOGY:

After ingestion of this plant, there may be a transient oral burning sensation, although other symptoms may not appear for 2 hours or more. Further symptoms begin as a sore throat and a dry hacking cough which may be accompanied by salivation and thirst. General lassitude and incessant yawning may be observed. A transient feeling of warmth in the stomach and mouth preceeds severe abdominal cramping, nausea, repeated vomiting and diarrhea. The vomitus may contain considerable amounts of blood. Profuse salivation, diaphoresis, blurred vision, vertigo, and very difficult and labored respiration as well as convulsive tremors may be observed (38, 43).

TREATMENT:

If the patient is seen prior to the onset of vomiting, induce emesis and perform gastric lavage. Administer activated charcoal followed by a saline cathartic (i.e., sodium sulfate). Demulcents such as milk, egg white, or vegetable oil may help soothe and protect the gastrointestinal mucosa. After the symptoms of severe gastroenteritis have begun, treatment should be directed toward reducing the abdominal cramping. Appropriate fluid and electrolyte therapy will be necessary in order to prevent dehydration and possible shock. Few fatalities have resulted from ingestion of this plant and recovery is usually complete after 24 to 36 hours.

Sambucus canadensis — ELDERBERRY, AMERICAN ELDER (Fig. 70 a, b, c)

DESCRIPTION:
This plant appears either as a shrub with many branches coming from the base of the plant or as a tree. The stems and twigs are green and contain a white pith inside the stem. Flowers are borne in large terminal, flattened clusters of small white flowers. Small dark purple-to-black berries that are bittersweet in flavor follow the flowers. The leaves (4 - 12 inches long) are made up of 5 - 11 leaflets arranged in opposite fashion, each ranging from 2 - 6 inches long. Leaflet margins are sharply serrated. The upper leaflet surface is bright green and lustrous, while the underside is paler and covered with short, fine plant hairs which give the leaflet the feel of fine velvet. The elderberry is found in vegetation areas 1, 2, 3, 4, 5, 6 and 7.

GENERAL:
The leaves, stems, and roots of this plant contain toxic substances. The immature berries and flowers are less toxic. The toxic principles have not been adequately characterized, but a cyanogenic glycoside and an alkaloid have been isolated. The cyanogenic glycoside is present in only a relatively low concentration. The ripe berries may produce nausea if ingested in any quantity. When cooked they are edible. Jams, jellies, and homemade wine have been prepared from the berries. There have been incidents of poisoning among children as a result of their removal of the white pith from the stem and subsequent use of the stems for blowguns, whistles, and popguns.

SYMPTOMATOLOGY:
Ingestion of the toxic portions of this plant produces signs of gastroenteritis with nausea, vomiting, and diarrhea being the chief symptoms. The possibility of cyanide poisoning should be borne in mind and treated appropriately should symptoms appear.

TREATMENT:
If the patient is seen soon after ingestion, induce emesis and perform gastric lavage. Administer activated charcoal and a saline cathartic. Thereafter, demulcents for the gastroenteritis are indicated. Cyanide poisoning may have to be treated with sodium nitrite and sodium thiosulfate as described elsewhere in this text.

69

Ranunculus spp. — **BUTTERCUP, CROWFOOT** (Fig. 60 a, b)

DESCRIPTION:
This annual or perennial herb usually attains a height of not over 3 feet, though some species are only 1 foot tall. The terminally located, frequently solitary flowers are usually bright yellow, although white and rarely red forms may be encountered. Each flower usually has 5 petals, although differing numbers of petals can be found on the flowers of the same plant. The leaves of this genus are palmate in shape. This plant is one of the more common weeds of the open pastures and damp marshy areas. The buttercup is found in vegetation areas 1, 2, 3, 4, 5, 6, 7, 8, 9 and 10.

GENERAL:
The fact that there are many known species of this plant that produce poisoning makes the entire genus suspect. A highly vesicant substance is formed within the plant by enzymatic cleavage of the glucoside ranunculin; causing the entire plant to be toxic (46). The resulting toxic substance, protoanemonin, is rendered inactive by drying or cooking. Varying concentrations of protoanemonin are found in the different species of the buttercup. The stage of growth also influences the protoanemonin content. The highest concentrations are found during the flowering stage (74). The acrid taste of these plants helps to reduce the probability of ingestion by children.

PROTOANEMONIN

SYMPTOMATOLOGY:
Crushing this plant releases the oily vesicant protoanemonin which produces severe irritation of mucous membranes, manifested initially as a burning sensation in the mouth and pharynx. This is followed by salivation, stomatitis, and frequently blistering and ulceration. Vomiting, gastroenteritis with abdominal pain, and frequently, bloody diarrhea are seen. Once absorbed from the gastrointestinal tract, protoanemonin produces dizziness, fainting, and frequently convulsions. Phemphigus eruptions may appear after severe systemic poisoning (56, 57). Severe dermatitis with vesiculation and pain may also occur after extended contact with the plant (44). Due to renal excretion of the toxic substances, kidney irritation produces polyuria initially, followed by urinary tract inflammation with hematuria and pain. Oliguria due to renal damage may occur (57).

TREATMENT:
Ingestion of this plant calls for induction of emesis if vomiting has not already occurred. Perform careful gastric lavage and administer activated charcoal. Administer demulcents such as milk, egg white, aluminum hydroxide gel, *et cetera.* Replacement of fluid and electrolyte deficits may be necessary if the symptoms become severe. Monitoring of renal function is essential.

Zygadenus nuttallii — **DEATH CAMAS** (Fig. 66)

DESCRIPTION:
This perennial herb has grass-like leaves and a single stem that is produced at the time of flowering. The 1 - 2 1/2 feet stalk bears a terminal cluster of yellowish-white flowers that appear from late February to early April. At the base of the stalk is a onion-like bulb or rhizome. The death camas is found in vegetation areas 1, 2, 3, 4, 5 and 7.

GENERAL:
The bulb of this plant is the portion most often involved in poisoning. It is frequently mistaken for a wild onion by the uninitiated with potentially fatal results. The bulb, with its dark outer covering, resembles an onion somewhat, but does not have an onion-like odor. The flowers and leaves can also produce toxicity (15).

SYMPTOMATOLOGY:
Immediate oral burning may occur, although symptoms may be delayed for up to 5 hours. Anorexia and salivation followed by vomiting and diarrhea may be seen. Drowsiness, headache, hypothermia, weakness, and dimness of vision have been seen. A prickling sensation of the skin may also occur. Bradycardia may occur, followed by severe hypotension and coma (57).

TREATMENT:
If spontaneous vomiting did not occur, induce emesis and perform gastric lavage even if symptoms have not developed. Administer activated charcoal and follow with a saline cathartic such as sodium sulfate. The bradycardia which is frequently present responds variably to atropine. In selected instances the bradycardia was not relieved by the administration of atropine (57). Pressor agents may be necessary for maintenance of blood pressure. External heat may be necessary to maintain normal body temperature. Symptomatic and supportive therapy is indicated thereafter. In most cases recovery is essentially complete in about 24 hours.

Toxicodendron quercifolium — **POISON OAK** (Fig. 72 a, b)
(Rhus quercifolia)

Toxicodendron radicans — **POISON IVY** (Fig. 71 a, b)
(Rhus toxicodendron)

Toxicodendron vernix — **POISON SUMAC** (Fig. 73 a, b)
(Rhus vernix)

DESCRIPTION:
Toxicodendron quercifolium - **POISON OAK** - This plant is similar to poison ivy in that the leaves are trifoliate and lobed. The small yellow-green flowers are borne in dense clusters which are followed by clusters of small creamy-white berries. Both the leaves (particularly the underside) and twigs of the poison oak are densely pubescent (covered with short, soft, down-like hairs). This pubescence, and the fact that the leaf is often more lobed and leathery, helps to distinguish it from poison ivy. Poison oak usually appears as a low shrub frequently under 3 feet tall. The poison oak is found in vegetation areas 1, 3, 6, 8 and 10.

Toxicodendron radicans - **POISON IVY** - The leaves of this plant are trifoliate (and rarely 5-foliate). Their shape and size is quite variable, ranging from smooth-to-dentate or lobed leaf margins. The plant may appear either as a suberect shrub or a woody vine. It bears small greenish-white flowers in small clusters followed by small, waxy, dullish-white drupes (berries). The poison ivy is found in vegetation areas 1, 2, 3, 4, 5, 6, 7, 8 and 10.

Toxicodendron vernix - **POISON SUMAC** - This plant appears as a shrub or small tree which may attain 25 feet in height. The leaves are composed of 7 - 13 alternately arranged leaflets that are 2 1/2 - 4 inches long and 1 - 2 inches wide. These leaflets have smooth margins. They are shiny above and somewhat pubescent underneath. The stems of the leaf and leaflets are frequently reddish in color. Its flowers are small and greenish resembling those of the poison ivy and are followed by a somewhat flattened greenish-white or gray drupe (berry). Poison sumac is found primarily in the pinewoods region of eastern Texas, vegetation area 1.

GENERAL:
The toxic principle which is found throughout these plants is the phenolic substance 3-pentadecylcatechol, commonly known as urushiol or toxicodendrol. All parts of the plant are toxic and remain so throughout the year. About 50% of the population is sensitive to topical contact with these plants (56), dermatitis being the chief complaint. That these plants are potent sensitizers is demonstrated by the fact that although a patient may

have previously been unaffected by the plant, subsequent contact may produce the characteristic lesions (82). Likewise, repeated contact in already sensitive individuals results in increasingly severe symptoms. Contact with the smoke produced by the burning of these plants can also produce toxicity.

The phenolic nature of urushiol makes for ready combination with the skin proteins. The old remedy of washing the contaminated area with yellow laundry soap, most likely serves only to remove any uncombined urushiol. Washing will not remove the already combined toxin, but may aid in prevention of further contamination of other body areas.

SYMPTOMATOLOGY:

Topical contact with these plants produces grouped erythematous papules and blotches surmounted by vesicles of various size. The onset of these eruptions may appear fairly rapidly (within 6 hours), although delays of several days are known (40). Chewing and/or ingestion of the leaves may produce severe swelling and blistering of the lips, tongue, buccal surfaces, and pharynx. Pain and difficulty in swallowing and talking may follow the oral contact (75). Vomiting and diarrhea as well as central nervous symptoms, including drowsiness, mydriasis, fever, delerium, and convulsion may also be present (2).

In very sensitive individuals the characteristic dermatitis has been accompanied with much more severe systemic manifestations. Renal complications ranging from glomerular nephritis to tubular degeneration with fatal anuria have been reported (71).

TREATMENT:

Treatment of the acute phase of the dermatological symptoms includes application of wet dressings utilizing Burow's solution (aluminum acetate solution) diluted 1 - 10 for adults and older children and 1 - 20 in younger children. Topical use of corticosteroid-containing creams may also be of considerable help in reducing the inflammation. Severe symptoms may require short-term oral corticosteroids. Oral antipruritic and antihistaminic agents may also help relieve some of the symptoms. Treatment, although reducing the symptoms somewhat, does not appreciably shorten the course of the affliction.

Should ingestion of the plant occur, induce emesis and administer activated charcoal. Perform gastric lavage using 1:5000 potassium permanganate and saline. Follow this with a saline cathartic. If systemic manifestations appear, treatment is mainly symptomatic and supportive. Urinary output should be monitored and indications of renal involvement should be watched for and treated accordingly.

Gelsemium sempervirens — **CAROLINA JESSAMINE, YELLOW JESSAMINE**
(Fig. 69 a, b)

DESCRIPTION:

This is an evergreen woody vine, either climbing or trailing, that may reach up to 20 feet in length. The leaves, which are dark green and shiny, have smooth margins and are usually 1 to 3 inches long and 1/2 - 1 inch wide. Bright yellow funnel-shaped flowers bloom in the early spring. The Carolina jessamine is found in vegetation areas 1 and 2.

GENERAL:

The entire plant contains the toxic alkaloids gelsemine, gelsemicine, and several other related alkaloids. Children have been severely poisoned by chewing the leaves, eating the flowers, and/or by sucking the nectar from the flowers (44, 57, 62). Honeybees have also been poisoned in this manner. The honey made from the nectar of the Carolina jessamine has been reported to be toxic (44).

GELSEMINE

SYMPTOMATOLOGY:

These alkaloids act primarily on the central nervous system, especially the spinal cord. Initially they stimulate and then depress motor centers (64). Symptoms of poisoning include headache, dizziness, mydriasis, ptosis, and diplopia or dimness of vision. Dryness of the mouth, profuse sweating, dysphagia, and inability to speak have been reported. Muscular weakness may be so severe that the patient may not be able to close his mouth. Due to the chemical similarity of these alkaloids to strychnine, some strychnine-like symptoms may be seen including muscular rigidity, trismus, and sometimes convulsions. The cardiac depressant effects of gelsemine may be seen as a reduction in the frequency and force of the pulse. Breathing may be considerably labored (44, 57, 64).

TREATMENT:

Induce emesis and perform gastric lavage. Administer activated charcoal and a saline cathartic (*i.e.,* sodium sulfate). Artificial respiration and oxygen therapy will most likely be needed to overcome the respiratory paralysis. Management of any strychnine-like effects may be necessary. Visual disturbances may continue for several days in those cases that do not end in fatality.

POISONOUS PLANTS

REFERENCES

1. Alexander, R. F., G. B. Forbes and E. S. Hawkins. "A Fatal Case of Solanine Poisoning". *Brit. Med. J.* 2:519 (1948).

2. Altschule, M.D. "The Genus *Rhus*". *Med. Sci.* 15:41 (1964).

3. Anonymous. "Toxicity Studies of Arizona Ornamental Plants". *Arizona Med.* 15:512-513 (1958).

4. Augenklin, R. B. "Augenverletzung Mit Dem Saft Der Pflanze *Dieffenbachia Seguine*". *Deutsch. Gesundh.* 26:73-76 (1971).

5. Balint, G. "Examination of Changes in the Magnesium Level of the Blood in Cats Poisoned with Ricin". *Med. Pharmacol. Exp.* (Basel). 17:183-188 (1967).

6. Balthrop, E. "Tung Nut Poisoning". *Southern Med. J.* 45:864-865 (1952).

7. Balthrop, E., W. B. Gallagher, T. F. McDonald and S. Camariotes. "Tung Nut Poisoning". *J. Florida Med. Ass.* 40:813-820 (1954).

8. Balucani, M. and D. D. Zeller. "Podophyllum Resin Poisoning with Complete Recovery". *J. A. M. A.* 189:639-640 (1964).

9. Barker, B. E., P. Farnes and P. H. LaMarche. "Peripheral Blood Plasmacytosis following Systemic Exposure to *Phytolacca americana* (Pokeweed)". *Pediatrics.* 38:490-493 (1966).

10. Berlin, C. M., Jr. "The Treatment of Cyanide Poisoning in Children". *Pediatrics.* 46:793-796 (1970).

11. Bowman, W. C. and I. S. Sanghvi. "Pharmacological Actions of Hemlock *(Conium Maculatum)* Alkaloids". *J. Pharm. Pharmacol.* 15:1-25 (1963).

12. Brady, E. T., Jr. "A Note on Morning Glory Seed Intoxication". *Amer. J. Hosp. Pharm.* 25:88-89 (1968).

13. Burton, L. E., A. L. Picchioni and L. Chin. "Dipotassium Edetate as an Antidote in Poisoning from Oleander and its Chief Glycoside, Oleandrin". *Arch. Int. Pharmacodyn. Ther.* 158:202-211 (1965).

14. Calderon-Gonzalez, R. and H. Rizzi-Hernandez. "Buckthorn Polyneuropathy". *New Eng. J. Med.* 277:69-71 (1967).

15. Cameron, K. "Death Camas Poisoning". *Northwest Med.* 51:682 (1952).

16. Campbell, E. W. "Plant Poisoning Umbelliferae (parsley family)". *J. Maine Med. Ass.* 57:40-42 (1966).

17. Carey, F. M., J. J. Lewis, J. L. MacGregor and M. Martin-Smith. "Pharmacological and Chemical Observations on Some Toxic Nectars". *J. Pharm. Pharmacol.* 11:269T-274T (1959).

18. Charlton, K. M. and K. R. Pierce. "A Neuropathy in Goats Caused by Experimental Coyotillo *(Karwinskia humboldtiana)* Poisoning". *Path. Vet.* 7:408-419 (1970).

19. Charlton, K. M., K. R. Pierce, R. W. Storts and C. H. Bridges. "A Neuropathy in Goats Caused by Experimental Coyotillo *(Karwinskia humboldtiana)"*. *Path. Vet.* 7:435-447 (1970).

20. Clark, A. N. G. and M. J. Parsonage. "Case of Podophyllum Poisoning with Involvement of Nervous System". *Brit. Med. J.* 2:1155 (1957).

21. Claus, E. P. *Pharmacognosy.* Lea and Febiger, Philadelphia, 4th ed., 1961, p. 312.

22. Cohen, S. "Suicide Following Morning Glory Seed Ingestion". *Amer. J. Psychiat.* 120:1024-1025 (1964).

23. Coruh, M. and A. Gonull. "Case Report of Podophyllin Poisoning". *Turk J. Pediat.* 6-7:100-103 (1964-1965).

24. Corwin, A. H. "Toxic Constituents of the Castor Bean". *J. Med. Pharm. Chem.* 4:483-496 (1961).

25. Cromwell, B. T. "The Separation, Micro-Estimation and Distribution of the Alkaloids of Hemlock *(Conium maculatum L.)"*. *Biochem. J.* 64:259-266 (1956).

26. DeBoer, J. "The Death of Socrates. A Historical and Experimental Study on the Actions of Coniine and *Conium Maculatum"*. *Arch Int. Pharmacodyn. Ther.* 83:473-490 (1950).

27. Der Marderosian, A. H. "Poisonous Plants In and Around the Home". *Amer. J. Pharm.* 30:115-140 (1966).

28. Dewan, M. L., J. B. Henson, J. W. Dollahite and C. H. Bridges. "Toxic Myodegeneration in Goats Produced by Feeding Mature Fruits from the Coyotillo Plant *(Karwinskia humboldtiana)"*. *Amer. J. Path.* 46:215-222 (1965).

29. Dore, W. G. "Crystalline Raphides in the Toxic Houseplant *Dieffenbachia*". *J. A. M. A.* 185:1045 (1963).

30. Dorsey, C. S. "Plant Dermatitis in California". *Cal. Med.* 96:412-413 (1962).

31. Drach, G. and W. H. Maloney. "Toxicity of the Common Houseplant *Dieffenbachia*". *J. A. M. A.* 184:1047 (1963).

32. Dreisbach, R. H. *Handbook of Poisoning.* Lange Medical Publications, Los Altos, California, 7th ed., 1971. *Cicuta,* pp. 424-425, *Ricinus,* p. 422.

33. Drysdale, R. G., P. R. Herrick and D. Franks. "The Specificity of the Haemagglutinin of the Castor Bean, *Ricinus communis*". *Vox. Sang.* 15:194-202 (1968).

34. Edwards, R. O. "Poisoning From Plant Ingestion". *J. Florida Med. Ass.* 52:875 (1965).

35. Ellis, M.D. "Treating Toxicity from Christmas Plants". *Hospital Physician,* 8:41-43 (1972).

36. Emery, Z. T. "Poisoning By Locust Bark". *New York Med. J.* 45:92 (1887).

37. Fochtman, F. W., J. E. Manno, C. L. Winek and J. A. Cooper. "Toxicology of the Genus *Dieffenbachia*". *Toxic. Appl. Pharmacol.* 15:30 (1969).

38. French, C. "Pokeroot Poisoning". *New York State Med. J.* 72:653-654 (1900).

39. Fuchs, V. L., M. Wichtl and G. Peithner. "Vergleichende chemische und biologische Untersuchung verschiedener Drogenmuster von *Convallaria majalis*". *Arzneimittel Forchung.* 13:220 (1963).

40. Gellin, G. A., R. Wolf and T. H. Milby. "Poison Ivy, Poison Oak, and Poison Sumac". *Arch Environ. Health.* 22:280-286 (1971).

41. Goldman, L., R. H. Preston and H. R. Muegel, "Dermatitis Venenata From English Ivy *(Hedera Helix)*". *Arch. Derm.* 74:311-312 (1956).

42. Goodman, L. S. and A. Gillman. *The Pharmacologic Basis of Therapeutics.* The MacMillan Co., London, 4th ed., 1970. *Convallaria,* pp. 692-693, *Datura,* p. 535, *Digitalis,* pp. 692-693, *Lobelia,* pp. 587, 590, *Lophophora,* p. 195, *Prunus,* pp. 934-936, *Pyrus,* pp. 934-936.

43. Guthrie, A. "Poisoning by Poke Root". *J. A. M. A.* 9:125 (1887).

44. Hardin, J. W. and J. M. Arena. *Human Poisoning from Native and Cultivated Plants.* Duke University Press, Durham, N.C., 1969. *Aesculus,* pp. 40-42,

Arisaema, pp. 40-42. *Cestrum,* p. 113, *Conium,* pp. 86-88, *Digitalis,* p. 121, *Gelsemium,* p. 102, *Hedera,* pp. 83-84, *Hyacinthus,* p. 38, *Hydrangea,* p. 59, *Ilex,* p. 74, *Iris,* p. 14, *Lathyrus,* p. 65, *Lophophora,* pp. 56-57, *Melia,* pp. 77-78, *Momordica,* pp. 88-89, *Poinciana,* p. 66, *Prunus,* p. 182, *Ranunculus,* p. 14, *Rhododendron,* pp. 98-100, *Ricinius,* pp. 96-98, *Robinia,* p. 66, *Sophora,* p. 68, *Wisteria,* pp. 69-70.

45. Hebanowski, M. "Przypadek ostrej nie domogi nerek w przebiegu zatrucia nasionami racznika". *Pol. Tyg. Lek.* 19:1204-1205 (1964).

46. Hill, R. and R. Van Heyningen. "Ranunculin: The Precursor of the Vesicant Substance of the Buttercup". *Biochem. J.* 49:332-335 (1951).

47. Hoch, J. H. "Poisonous Plants in South Carolina. 3.". *J. S. Carolina Med. Ass.* 61:142-143 (1965).

48. Ingram, A. L., Jr. "Morning Glory Seed Reaction". *J. A. M. A.* 190:1133-1134 (1964).

49. Jacobziner, H. and H. W. Raybin. "Briefs on Accidental Chemical Poisonings in New York City". *New York State J. Med.* 61:2463-2466 (1961).

50. Jacobziner, H. and H. W. Raybin. "Intoxications Due to Tranquilizing Drugs and Plants". *New York State J. Med.* 62:3130-3132 (1962).

51. Jacobziner, H. and H. W. Raybin. "Rhubarb Poisoning". *New York State J. Med.* 62:1676-1678 (1962).

52. Kabat, E. A., M. Heidelberger and A. E. Bezer. "A Study of the Purification and Properties of Ricin". *J. Biol. Chem.* 168:629-639 (1947).

53. Kalliala, H. and O. Kauste. "Ingestion of Rhubarb Leaves as Cause of Oxalic Acid Poisoning". *Ann. Paediat. Fenn.* 10:228-231 (1964).

54. Kapadia, G. J. and B. E. Fayez. "Peyote Constitutents: Chemistry, Biogenesis, and Biological Effects". *J. Pharm. Sci.* 59:1699-1722 (1970).

55. Kim, H. L. and B. J. Camp. "Isolation of a Neurotoxic Substance from *Karwinskia Humboldtiana* Zucc. (Rhamnaceae)". *Toxicon.* 10:83-84 (1972).

56. Kingsbury, J. M. *Poisonous Plants of the United States and Canada,* Prentice-Hall, Inc., Englewood Cliffs, N. J., 1964. *Arisaema,* p. 472, *Cestrum,* p. 273, *Conium,* pp. 379-383, *Dieffenbachia,* pp. 473-475, *Hedera,* pp. 371-372, *Hydrangea,* pp. 23-26, 370-371, *Lathyrus,* pp. 329-331, *Melia,* pp. 206-208, *Momordica,* p. 389, *Narcissus,* p. 468, *Parthenocissus,* pp. 34-35, 221-222, *Phytolacca,* pp. 225-227, *Prunus,* pp. 23-26, 365-370, *Pyrus,* pp. 23-26, 365, *Rheum,* 34-35, 230-231, *Rhododendron,* p. 255-260, *Robinia,* pp.

351-353, *Sesbania,* pp. 354-357, *Solanum,* pp. 287-289, *Sophora,* p. 358, *Toxicodendron,* p. 213.

57. Lampe, K. and R. Fagerström. *Plant Toxicity and Dermatitis,* The Williams and Wilkins Co., Baltimore, Maryland, 1968. *Arisaema,* pp. 11-18, *Cestrum,* pp. 118-121, *Convallaria,* 88-89, *Delphinium,* pp. 94-96, *Dieffenbachia,* pp. 11-18, *Digitalis,* p. 87, *Gelsemium,* p. 177, *Ilex,* p. 53, *Iris,* pp. 35, 37, *Ligustrum,* pp. 53-54, *Lobelia,* pp. 114-115, *Melia,* pp. 132-133, *Momordica,* pp. 22-23, *Narcissus,* pp. 194, 196, *Nerium,* pp. 88-89, *Parthenocissus,* pp. 78-79, *Phytolacca,* pp. 27, 31-34, *Podophyllum,* pp. 34-35, *Poinciana,* pp. 48, 51, *Ranunculus,* pp. 40-41, *Rheum,* pp. 78-79, *Ricinus,* pp. 62-63, *Wisteria,* p. 19, *Zygadenus,* pp. 102-103.

58. Meiring, P. DeV. "Poisoning by *Datura Stramonium".* *S. Afr. Med. J.* 40:311-312 (1966).

59. Mitchell, J. E. and F. N. Mitchell, "Jimson Weed *(Datura Stramonium)* Poisoning in Childhood". *J. Pediat.* 47:227 (1955).

60. Mladoveanu, C., O. Vasilco and P. Gheorghu. "Le Sulfate de Magnesium et le chlorure de Calcium dans les Intoxications Experimentales avec l'Aconitine". *Arch. Int. Pharmacodyn. Ther.* 63:494-498 (1939).

61. Moore, H. W. "Mistletoe Poisoning". *J. S. Carolina Med. Ass.* 59:269-271 (1963).

62. Morton, J. F. "Ornamental Plants with Poisonous Properties". *Proc. Florida State Hort. Soc.* 71:372 (1958).

63. Muenscher, W. C. *Poisonous Plants of the United States,* The MacMillan Co., New York, 1966. *Cicuta,* pp. 173-177, *Ligustrum,* p. 190.

64. Osol, A. and G. E. Farrar. *United States Dispensatory,* 25th ed., J. B. Lippincott Co., Philadelphia, 1955. *Gelsemium* pp. 1704-1705, *Lobelia,* pp. 767-769.

65. Pike, M. "The Effect of an Alcoholic Extract of the Leaves of *Phytolacca Americana* on Mecamylamine Toxicity in Mice and Rats". *Exp. Med. Surg.* 28:154-162 (1970).

66. Pohl, R. W. "Poisoning by *Dieffenbachia".* *J. A. M. A.* 177:162 (1961).

67. Robson, P. and M. B. Lond. "Water Hemlock Poisoning". *Lancet.* 2:1274-1275 (1965).

68. Rork, L. E. "Plant Poisoning in a Child". *Rocky Mountain Med. J.* 66:47-49 (1969).

69. Rosen, C. S. and M. Lechner. "Jimson-Weed Intoxication". *New Eng. J. Med.* 267:448-450 (1962).

70. Russell, L. H., W. L. Schwartz and J. W. Dollahite. "Toxicity of Chinese Tallow Tree *(Sapium sebiferum)* for Ruminants". *Amer. J. Vet. Res.* 30: 1233-1238 (1969).

71. Rytand, D. A. "Fatal Anuria, The Nephrotic Syndrome and Glomerular Nephritis as Sequels of the Dermatitis of Poison Oak". *Amer. J. Med.* 5:548-560 (1948).

72. Sayre, J. W. and S. Kaymakcalan. "Cyanide Poisoning from Apricot Seeds among Children in Central Turkey". *New Eng. J. Med.* 270:1113-1115 (1964).

73. Schweitzer, H. "Todliche Saponinvergiftung durch Genuss von Rosskastanien". *Med. Klin.* 47:683 (1952).

74. Shearer, G. D. "Some Observations on the Poisoning of Buttercups". *Vet. J.* 94:22 (1938).

75. Silvers, S. H. "Stomatitis Venenata and Dermatitis of the Anal Orifice From Chewing Poison Ivy Leaves *(Rhus Toxicodendron)*". *J. A. M. A.* 116:2257 (1941).

76. Simpson, K. *Taylor's Principles and Practice of Medical Jurisprudence.* J. & A. Churchill Ltd., London, 1964, p. 508.

77. Sollmann, T. *A Manual of Pharmacology,* 8th ed., W. B. Saunders, Philadelphia, 1957, pp. 667-669, *Ricinus,* pp. 213-214.

78. Sperry, O. E., J. W. Dollahite, G. O. Hollman and B. J. Camp. "Texas Plants Poisonous to Livestock". *Texas Agri. Expt. Sta. Bull.* B-1028 (1964) pp. 6-7.

79. Stecher, P. G., Ed. *The Merck Index,* Merck & Company, Inc. Rahway, N.J., 8th ed., 1968. *Datura,* p. 983, *Phytolacca,* p. 830.

80. Stone, R. P. and W. J. Collins. "*Euphorbia pulcherrima:* Toxicity to Rats". *Toxicon.* 9:301-302 (1971).

81. Tallqvist, H. and K. Vaananen. "Death of a Child from Oxalic Acid Poisoning due to Eating Rhubarb Leaves". *Ann. Paediat. Fenn.* 6-7:144-147 (1960-1961).

82. Turner, C. E. "Rhus Dermatitis as a Public Health and Health Education Problem". *Amer. J. Pub. Health.* 37:7-12 (1947).

83. Vines, R. A. *Trees Shrubs and Woody Vines of the Southwest.* University of Texas Press, Austin, 1960. *Sapium,* p. 622, *Sophora,* p. 569.

84. von Oettingen, W. F. *Poisoning,* W. B. Saunders Co., Philadelphia, London, 1958. *Delphinium,* pp. 324-325, *Solanum,* pp. 539-540.

85. Walter, W. G. "Dieffenbachia Toxicity". *J. A. M. A.* 201:140 (1967).

86. Watt, J. M., H. L. Heimann and E. Epstein. "Solanocapsine - A New Alkaloid with a Cardiac Action". *Quart. J. Pharm. Pharmacol.* 5:649 (1932).

87. Waud, R. A. "The Action of Kalmia Agustifolia (Lambkill)". *J. Pharmacol. Exp. Ther.* 69:103-111 (1940).

88. West, E. "Poisonous Plants Around the Home". *Florida Agri. Expt. Sta. Bull.* 175 (1960). *Aleurites,* pp. 35-36, *Datura,* pp. 19-21, *Hydrangea,* pp. 16-17, *Nerium,* pp. 27-29.

89. West, E. and W. M. Emmel. "Some Poisonous Plants in Florida". *Florida Agri. Expt. Sta. Bull.* 468 (1952), pp. 7-9.

90. Wolfson, S. L. and T. W. G. Solomons. "Poisoning by Fruits of Lantana Camara". *Amer. J. Dis. Child.* 107:173 (1964).

91. Wood, H. B., Jr., V. L. Stromberg, J. C. Keresztesy and E. C. Horning. "Andromedotoxin. A Potent Hypotensive Agent from *Rhododendron maximum". J. Amer. Chem. Soc.* 76:5689-5692 (1954).

92. Yashina, N. M. "Sravnibel' naya otsenka serdechnykh glyukozidov". *Ref. Zh. Otd. Vypusk. Farmakol. Toksikol.* No. 20.54.109. (1964).

VEGETATION AREAS OF TEXAS

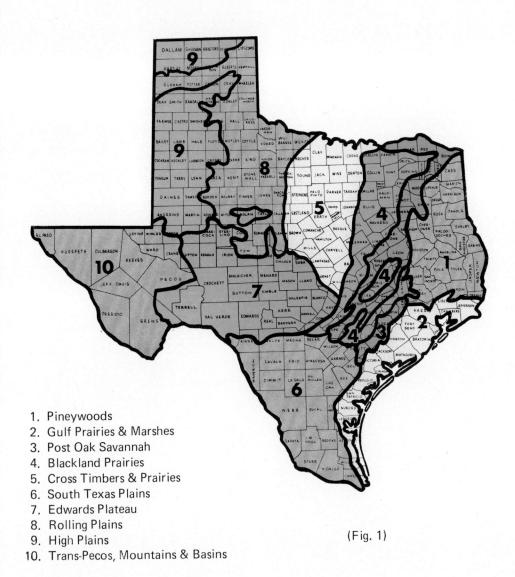

1. Pineywoods
2. Gulf Prairies & Marshes
3. Post Oak Savannah
4. Blackland Prairies
5. Cross Timbers & Prairies
6. South Texas Plains
7. Edwards Plateau
8. Rolling Plains
9. High Plains
10. Trans-Pecos, Mountains & Basins

(Fig. 1)

(From, Texas Plants - A Checklist & Ecological Summary, By Frank Gould, Texas A & M Univ., Texas Agri. Expt. Stat., Bull. MP - 585/Revised April, 1969)

Fig. 2 a. DIEFFEN-
BACHIA, DUMBCANE
(Dieffenbachia picta,
'Rudolph roehrs')

Fig. 2 b. DIEFFENBACHIA,
DUMBCANE *(Dieffenbachia*
picta superba)

Fig. 2 c. DIEFFEN-
BACHIA, DUMB-
CANE *(Dieffen-*
bachia jenmanii)

Fig. 3 a. PHILODENDRON
(Philodendron squamiferum)

Fig. 3 b. PHILODENDRON
*(Philodendron oxycardium
'cordatum')*

Fig. 3 c. PHILODENDRON
(Philodendron 'Burgundy')

Fig. 3 d. SPLIT - LEAF PHILODENDRON
(Philodendron bipinnatifidum)

Fig. 4. ELEPHANT'S EAR *(Colocasia sp.)*

Fig. 5. SPLIT-LEAF PHILODENDRON, CERIMAN *(Monstera deliciosa)*

Fig. 6. ELEPHANT'S EAR *(Caladium sp.)*

Fig. 7. FANCY-LEAF CALADIUM *(Caladium spp.)*

Fig. 8 a. CASTOR BEAN
(Ricinus sp.)

Fig. 8 b. CASTOR BEANS & SEED PACKAGE

Fig. 8 c. CASTOR BEAN LEAF &
CAPSULE   *(Ricinus communis)*

Fig. 8 d. CASTOR BEAN
(Ricinus sp.)

Fig. 9. NIGHT-BLOOMING JESSAMINE *(Cestrum nocturnum)*

Fig. 10. DAY-BLOOMING JESSAMINE
(Cestrum diurnum)

Fig. 11. ENGLISH IVY *(Hedera helix)*

Fig. 12 a. LANTANA
(Lantana sp.)

Fig. 12 b. LANTANA FLOWERS

Fig. 12 c. LANTANA *(Lantana camara)*

Fig. 12 d. LANTANA
BERRIES, LEAVES

Fig. 13. TUNG NUT
(Aleurites fordii)

Fig. 14 a.
DIGITALIS,
FOXGLOVE
*(Digitalis
purpurea)*

(Photo by C. C. Albers)

(Photo by R. J. Neubauer)

Fig. 14 b. DIGITALIS
FLOWER *(Digitalis
purpurea)*.

Fig. 14 c. DIGITALIS SEEDS
& SEED PACKAGE.

Fig. 15 a. AZALEA
(Rhododendron sp.)

Fig. 15 b. RHODODENDRON
(Rhododendron sp.)

(Photo by R. J. Neubauer)

Fig. 15 c. RHODO-
DENDRON
(Rhododendron sp.)

(Photo by R. J. Neubauer)

Fig. 16 a. LARKSPUR *(Delphinium sp.)*

Fig. 16 b. LARKSPUR
(Delphinium sp.)

Fig. 16 c. LARKSPUR SEEDS & SEED PACKAGE
(Delphinium sp.)

Fig. 17 a. POINSETTIA (Red
Variety) *(Euphorbia pulcherrima)*

Fig. 17 b. POINSETTIA (White
Variety) *(Euphorbia pulcherrima)*

Fig. 18. APPLE; FRUIT & SEEDS *Pyrus sylvestris)*

Fig. 19 a. HYDRANGEA
(Hydrangea macrophylla)

Fig. 19 b. HYDRANGEA
(Hydrangea macrophylla)

Fig. 19 c. HYDRANGEA LEAVES
(Hydrangea macrophylla)

Fig. 20 a. LILY - OF - THE - VALLEY *(Convallaria majalis)*

Fig. 20 b. LILY - OF - THE - VALLEY *(Convallaria majalis)*

Fig. 21 a. SWEET PEA *(Lathyrus odoratus)*

Fig. 21 b. SWEET PEA SEEDS & SEED PACKAGE *(Lathyrus odoratus)*

Fig. 22 a. HOLLY *(Ilex cornuta)*

(Photo by M. Wichman)

Fig. 22 b. HOLLY *(Ilex opaca)*

Fig. 23. YAUPON
(Ilex vomitoria)

Fig. 24. MORNING GLORY
SEEDS & SEED PACKAGE
(Ipomoea violacea)

Fig. 25. HYACINTH
(Hyacinthus orientalis)

Fig. 26. IRIS *(Iris sp.)*

Fig. 27 b. LIGUSTRUM
'BERRIES' *(Ligustrum
sp.)*

Fig. 27 a. LIGUSTRUM *(Ligustrum sp.)*

Fig. 28. DAFFODIL, JONQUIL,
NARCISSUS *(Narcissus sp.)*

Fig. 29 a. POINCIANA, BIRD-OF-PARADISE *(Poinciana gilliesii)*

Fig. 29 b. POINCIANA FLOWER & SEED POD *(Poinciana gilliesii)*

Fig. 30 a. WISTERIA *(Wisteria sp.)*

Fig. 30 b. WISTERIA FLOWER, LEAF & SEED *(Wisteria sp.)*

Fig. 30 c. WISTERIA SEED POD *(Wisteria sp.)*

Fig. 31 a. CHINABERRY
TREE FLOWERS & LEAVES
(Melia azedarach)

Fig. 31 b. UNRIPE
CHINABERRIES &
L E A V E S *(Melia*
azedarach)

Fig. 31 c. MATURE
CHINABERRIES
(Melia azedarach)

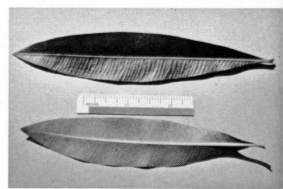

Fig. 32 b. OLEANDER LEAVES
(Nerium oleander)

Fig. 32 a. OLEANDER FLOWERS *(Nerium oleander)*

Fig. 32 c. OLEANDER
(Nerium oleander)

Fig. 33. CHINESE TALLOW
TREE, TALLOW TREE
(Sapium sebiferum)

Fig. 34. WILD BLACK CHERRY
(Prunus serotina)

Fig. 35. CHERRY-LAUREL
(Prunus caroliniana)

Fig. 36. CHOKE
CHERRY
(Prunus virginiana)

Fig. 37. PEACH *(Prunus persica)*   Fig. 38. AMERICAN PLUM
(Prunus americana)

Fig. 39. CULTIVATED
CHERRY
(Prunus cerasus)

Fig. 40. APRICOT *(Prunus armeniaca)*

Fig. 41 b. JAPANESE YEW
'BERRIES' *(Podocarpus macrophylla)*

Fig. 41 a. JAPANESE YEW
(Podocarpus macrophylla)

Fig. 42. JERUSALEM
CHERRY *(Solanum
pseudocapsicum)*

Fig. 43. RHUBARB *(Rheum
raponticum)*

Fig. 44 a. RED BUCKEYE
(Aesculus pavia)

(Photo by M. Wichman)

Fig. 44 b. RED BUCKEYE SEED
(LARGE), T.EXAS BUCKEYE
SEED (SMALL)

Fig. 44 c. RED BUCKEYE
(Aesculus pavia)

Fig. 44 d. RED
BUCKEYE SEEDS
IN CAPSULE
(Aesculus pavia)

(Photo by M. Wichman)

Fig. 45 a. JACK - IN - THE - PULPIT
(Arisaema triphyllum)

(Photo by M. Wichman)

Fig. 45 b. JACK - IN - THE - PULPIT
(Arisaema triphyllum)

Fig. 46 b. MAYAPPLE,
MANDRAKE
(Podophyllum peltatum)

(Photo by M. Wichman)

Fig. 46 a. MAYAPPLE, MANDRAKE
(Podophyllum peltatum)

Fig. 47 a. WATER HEMLOCK
(Cicuta maculata)

Fig. 47 b. WATER HEMLOCK ROOT
(Cicuta maculata)

Fig. 47 c. WATER HEMLOCK FLOWERS

Fig. 47 d. WATER HEMLOCK
SEEDS

Fig. 47 e. WATER HEMLOCK
LEAVES *(Cicuta maculata)*
(Smaller at top of plant),
(Larger at base of plant)

Fig. 48 a. COYOTILLO, TULLIDORA *(Karwinskia humboldtiana)*

Fig. 48 b. COYOTILLO LEAF & BERRIES
(Karwinskia humboldtiana)

Fig. 48 c. COYOTILLO LEAVES & BERRIES

Fig. 48 d. COYOTILLO LEAF & BERRIES *(Karwinskia humboldtiana)*

Fig. 49 a. VIRGINIA CREEPER
(Parthenocissus quinquefolia)

Fig. 49 b. VIRGINIA CREEPER LEAF
(Parthenocissus quinquefolia)

Fig. 49 c. VIRGINIA CREEPER
(Parthenocissus quinquefolia)

Fig. 50. WILD BALSAM - APPLE
(Momordica charantia)

(From, "Plants Poisonous To People In Florida &
Other Warm Areas," Hurricane House Publishers,
Inc., Miami, Florida c 1970, Julia Morton)

(Photo by J. Weaver)

Fig. 51 b. POISON HEMLOCK
(Conium maculatum)

Fig. 51 a. POISON HEMLOCK
(Conium maculatum)

Fig. 51 c. POISON HEMLOCK LEAF
(Conium maculatum)

Fig. 51 d. POISON HEMLOCK LEAF
(Conium maculatum)

Fig. 51 e. POISON HEMLOCK
FLOWER (HALF-OPENED)
(Conium maculatum)

Fig. 52 a. MESCAL BEAN FLOWER
(Sophora secundiflora)

Fig. 52 b. MESCAL BEAN SEED & LEAF
(Sophora secundiflora)

Fig. 53 a. CAROLINA HORSENETTLE BERRY & LEAF
(Solanum carolinense)

Fig. 53 b. CAROLINA HORSENETTLE
(Solanum carolinense)

Fig. 54. AMERICAN MISTLETOE
(Phoradendron serotinum)

Fig. 55 a. SILVERLEAF NIGHTSHADE
(Solanum eleagnifolium)

Fig. 55 b. SILVERLEAF NIGHTSHADE BERRIES
(Solanum eleagnifolium)

Fig. 56 a. BLACK
NIGHTSHADE, AMERICAN
NIGHTSHADE *(Solanum
americanum)*

Fig. 56 b. BLACK
NIGHTSHADE BERRIES,
LEAVES, & FLOWERS
(Solanum americanum)

Fig. 57 b. SENNA-BEAN POD & FLOWER
(Sesbania drummondii)

Fig. 57 a. SENNA-BEAN
(Sesbania drummondii)

Fig. 58 a. PURPLE RATTLEBOX
(Sesbania punicea)

Fig. 58 b. PURPLE
RATTLEBOX FLOWER,
SEED POD, & SEEDS
(Sesbania punicea)

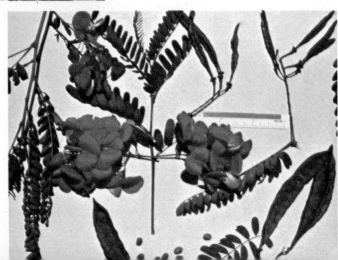

Fig. 59 a. BAGPOD,
BLADDERPOD *(Sesbania
vesicarium)*

Fig. 60 a. BUTTERCUP *(Ranunculus sp.)*

Fig. 59 b. BAGPOD SEEDS & SEEDPOD
(Sesbania vesicarium)

Fig. 60 b. BUTTERCUP FLOWER & LEAF
(Ranunculus sp.)

Fig. 61. PEYOTE, MESCAL
BUTTON *(Lophophora williamsii)*

Fig. 62 a. MOONFLOWER, ANGEL'S TRUMPET *(Datura meteloides)*

(Photo by M. Wichman)

Fig. 62 b. MOONFLOWER *(Datura meteloides)*

Fig. 62 c. MOONFLOWER LEAF & FRUIT *(Datura meteloides)*

Fig. 63. JIMSONWEED *(Datura stramonium)*

Fig. 64 a. BLACK LOCUST
(Robinia pseudoacacia)

(Photo by M. Wichman)

Fig. 64 b. BLACK LOCUST FLOWER
(Robinia pseudoacacia)

Fig. 64 c. BLACK LOCUST
SEED POD & SEEDS

Fig. 64 d. BLACK LOCUST LEAF & THORNY STEM
(Robinia pseudoacacia)

Fig. 64 e. BLACK LOCUST
LEAF & FLOWER
(Robinia pseudoacacia)

Fig. 65 a. TREE TOBACCO
(Nicotiana glauca)

Fig. 65 b. TREE TOBACCO LEAF
& FLOWER
(Nicotiana glauca)

(Photo by C. A. Rechenthin)

Fig. 66. DEATH CAMAS
(Zygadenus nuttallii)

(Photo by M. Wichman)

Fig. 67. CARDINAL FLOWER
(Lobelia cardinalis)

Fig. 68 a. POKEWEED,
POKEROOT *(Phytolacca
americana)*

Fig. 68 b. POKEWEED FLOWER,
BERRIES & LEAVES *(Phytolacca
americana)*

Fig. 69 a. CAROLINA JESSAMINE, YELLOW JESSAMINE
(Gelsemium sempervirens)

(Photo by C. A. Rechenthin)

Fig. 69 b. CAROLINA
JESSAMINE
(Gelsemium sempervirens)

Fig. 70 a. ELDERBERRY
(Sambucus canadensis)

Fig. 70 b. ELDERBERRY
FLOWER & BERRIES
(Sambucus canadensis)

Fig. 70 c. ELDERBERRY
LEAF, STEM, & FLOWER
(Sambucus canadensis)

Fig. 71 a. POISON IVY
(Toxicodendron radicans)

Fig. 71 b. POISON IVY *(Toxicodendron radicans)*

Fig. 72 a. POISON OAK
(Toxicodendron quercifolium)

Fig. 72 b. POISON OAK
(Toxicodendron quercifolium)

Fig. 73 a. POISON SUMAC *(Toxicodendron vernix)*

Fig. 73 b. POISON SUMAC LEAF & 'BERRY'
(Toxicodendron vernix)

VENOMOUS AND
NON-VENOMOUS SNAKES

VENOMOUS SNAKES

Ted T. Huang, M.D.
S. R. Lewis, M.D.
Baker Stephen Lucas, III, B.S.

INTRODUCTION
AND
GENERAL EPIDEMIOLOGY

There are approximately 7,000 people each year treated for poisonous snake-bite in the United States. One or more species of poisonous snakes are found in every state, with the exceptions of Maine, Hawaii and Alaska. Rattlesnakes account for about 75 percent of the total number of venomous bites; copperheads and cottonmouths are involved in about 23 percent of the bites. Coral snakes and foreign venomous snakes in captivity account for the remaining bites. Most of the venomous bites occur in the southeastern and southwestern states.

Rattlesnakes inhabit all the continental states except Alaska, Maine, Delaware and the District of Columbia. Copperheads are found in 29 states, located primarily in the eastern two thirds of the country. Cottonmouths are indigenous to only 16 southeastern and southwestern states. Coral snakes are also located in the southeast and southwest portions of the United States and are found in only 11 states. (15)

All of the poisonous snakes belong to the family *Crotalidae* (a notable exception being the coral snake, which is a member of the family *Elapidae*). The family *Crotalidae* are called pit vipers, due to an externally visible facial pit located below and back of the nostril. Pit vipers consist of the genera *Crotalus* and *Sistrurus* (the rattlesnakes), and the genus *Agkistrodon* (the copperheads and the cottonmouth water moccasin). The main distinction between *Crotalus* and *Sistrurus* is that the former has small scales on the crown of the head, while the latter has large plates. They both possess rattles which are "a loosely articulated, but interlocking, series of horny rings at the end of the tail, which, when vibrated, produces a hissing sound" (9). The copperheads and cottonmouth moccasin have large plates on the crown of their head and no rattles. They do, however, vibrate their tails in the manner of a rattler.

The family as a whole has a highly developed venom apparatus which consists of large, hollow, movable fangs located at the front of the upper jaw (Figure 74). When the snake strikes, these fangs are swung forward from a folded position and the prey is stabbed and envenomated in a rapid thrust (17).

The family *Elapidae* is represented in the Old World by such infamous members as the cobras, mambas, kraits and tiger snakes. The secretive coral snake proves a worthy representative of the group when one considers the potency of its venom. Drop for drop, the venom of the coral snake is considered more poisonous than that of the pit vipers. This family of snakes is characterized by rigid, short, grooved fangs located near the front of the mouth.

One must be careful when trying to distinguish the various species of poisonous snakes. For instance, identification by color is a hazardous venture at best. The Western Diamondback Rattlesnake is not only one of the most prevalent poisonous snakes, but it can be found in almost every color of the rainbow, ranging from reds

125

and browns to pale tans and grays. The best indicators for species identification are described in the text as the most prominent characteristics of each of the species. Usual colors are also given but they are to be used only as a guide and are by no means absolute. Remember, if a snake has a rattle on its tail, it is poisonous. If not, you have to look at the snake a little closer.

GENUS – *CROTALUS*

Crotalus atrox – **WESTERN DIAMONDBACK RATTLESNAKE** (Fig. 75 a, b, c, d)

DESCRIPTION:
The Western Diamondback Rattler is best noted for its distinct, alternating black and white rings on the tail just above the rattle. This snake has often been referred to as a "coontail rattler." A light stripe behind the eye reaches the lip in the front corner of the mouth. Since the diamond-shaped pattern is not clear-cut and distinct, the entire snake may possess an overall dusty or speckled appearance. This snake is responsible for most of the snakebites in the state and is quite aggressive if disturbed. The adult snake measures from 30 inches to 6 feet (weighing up to 24 pounds).

Crotalus horridus horridus – **TIMBER RATTLESNAKE** (Fig. 76 a, b)

DESCRIPTION:
The Timber Rattlesnake or "velvet-tail rattler" has two major color patterns. The yellow phase is the most prominent with brown or black bands on a background of yellow, brown, or gray. Somewhat "V-shaped" crossbanding begins anteriorly, breaking up about half way down the back of the snake into a row of dark spots. A row of dark spots is also seen on either side of the body of the snake.
The black phase is distinguished by a dark, brown-to-black, shadowy color in the interspaces between the crossbands. Some specimens are completely black. Generally there are no head markings on this rather large snake.

Crotalus horridus atricaudatus – **CANEBRAKE RATTLESNAKE** (Fig. 77 a, b, c)

DESCRIPTION:
The Canebrake rattler is characterized by a reddish stripe which runs down the spine of the snake. This stripe divides the black dorsal spots on the forward part of the body in half. This snake is characterized by a wide, dark stripe running posteriorly from the eye to the angle of the jaw and beyond. The ground color of the snake ranges from a greenish-brown to a pinkish-tan. The Canebrake rattler can attain considerable size, the record being around six feet in length.

Crotalus lepidus lepidus — **MOTTLED ROCK RATTLESNAKE** (Fig. 78 a, b, c)

DESCRIPTION:
 This is a very dusty appearing snake, with considerable dark spotting between dark body bands, which sometimes produces the effect of pseudo-crossbands between the primary ones. The crossbands are more prominent toward the tail. Its general coloration may vary from gray or bluish-gray to tan or pink. The Mottled Rock rattler usually does not attain a length of much over 2 feet.

Crotalus lepidus klauberi — **BANDED ROCK RATTLESNAKE** (Fig. 79 a, b, c)

DESCRIPTION:
 This small rattler has black or brown jagged crossbands which contrast sharply with a general ground color of greenish - gray. The interspaces between the crossbands are moderately speckled. The Banded Rock rattler is found only in far West Texas.

Crotalus molossus molossus — **NORTHERN BLACK-TAILED RATTLESNAKE** (Fig. 80 a, b)

DESCRIPTION:
 The Northern Black-tailed rattler is characterized by a solid black tail. In some, the snout of the snake is also black. The rest of the body has dark crossbands with patches or spots of light color appearing within the crossbands. Generally the background color is yellow, greenish, or olive. A unique thing about this snake is the fact that each individual scale has only one color with no evidence of a pattern change cutting across the scales. Sometimes diamond-shaped dark markings are seen on the anterior portion of the snake. The adult can attain a length of just over 4 feet.

Crotalus viridis viridis — **PRAIRIE RATTLESNAKE** (Fig. 81 a, b, c)

DESCRIPTION:
 The Prairie rattler is a medium-sized snake with black or brown blotches, usually having light-colored edges, which run down the back and narrow to form crossbands near the tail. A light stripe is seen beginning behind the eye and extending to behind the corner of the mouth. The background color of the snake varies throughout the habitat range with there being a tendency toward greenish-gray, olive green, or greenish-brown.

Crotalus scutulatus scutulatus — **MOJAVE RATTLESNAKE** (Fig. 82 a, b, c)

DESCRIPTION:

This medium-sized rattlesnake has generally well defined, light-edged diamonds or hexagons which run down the middle of the back. A light stripe extends from behind the eye to behind the corner of the mouth. The tail has light and dark rings with the dark rings being narrower than the light ones. The ground color varies from greenish-gray to brown. The Mojave rattler is confined to areas of far West Texas.

GENUS — *SISTRURUS*

Sistrurus catenatus tergeminus — **WESTERN MASSASAUGA** (Fig. 83 a, b, c)

DESCRIPTION:

The Western Massasauga has approximately 39 dark brown blotches centered in a gray-to-tan ground color. The blotches are narrowly edged with a lighter color. Rows of smaller and lighter spots appear on each side of the body. These snakes are relatively small and seldom attain 3 feet in length, with the average being around 2 feet.

Sistrurus catenatus edwardsi — **DESERT MASSASAUGA** (Fig. 84 a, b, c)

DESCRIPTION:

The Desert Massasauga is a lighter colored species than the Western Massasauga. Its belly is pale and either plain or lightly flecked with gray or brown. The blotches described under the Western Massasauga are still apparent in this species, although they are much paler in color. The Desert Massasauga is a small snake and seldom reaches much more than 2 1/2 feet in length.

Sistrurus miliarius streckeri — **WESTERN PIGMY RATTLESNAKE** (Fig. 85 a, b)

DESCRIPTION:

The Western Pigmy rattler is usually distinguished by a reddish dorsal stripe which extends down the spine to the tail, although this stripe has been known to be absent in species. The stripe divides about 35 small, dark, narrow spots or crossbars. The crossbars become less distinct further down the tail. One or two rows of smaller dark spots appear on the side of the body and run the entire length of the snake. The general ground color is a light, pale gray to grayish-brown. The Western Pigmy rattler seldom attains a length of over 2 feet. Its rattle is very tiny and produces a high pitched sound usually not audible to human ears. Its favorite habitat is swampland or waterways. Its irritable, aggressive temperment makes it quick to strike if disturbed.

GENUS — *AGKISTRODON*

Agkistrodon contortrix contortrix — **SOUTHERN COPPERHEAD** (Fig. 86 a, b)

DESCRIPTION:
 The Southern Copperhead is lighter in color than the other copperheads. The hourglass markings are quite narrow across the back of the snake. Frequently the markings are broken middorsally with the two halves failing to meet. The ground color is light brown or tan with a pinkish tinge. Adult snakes average between 20 - 36 inches in length.

Agkistrodon contortrix laticinctus — **BROADBANDED COPPERHEAD** (Fig. 87 a, b)

DESCRIPTION:
 The crossbands of the Broadbanded copperhead are easily distinguished from the other forms because they are very broad and straight-edged. The bands are usually a rich reddish-brown or chestnut, with the tip of the tail being yellowish-green to greenish-gray. The body color is much lighter than the crossbands, while the belly is about the same color as the bands. Adult snakes can reach a length of 3 feet, but most average about 2 feet.

Agkistrodon contortrix mokasen — **NORTHERN COPPERHEAD** (Fig. 88 a, b)

DESCRIPTION:
 The Northern copperhead has a coppery-red head with hour-glass-shaped markings of reddish-brown or chestnut-colored crossbands. These "hourglasses" are rounded at the base. Dark rounded spots appear at the sides of the belly. The belly is dark and mottled with dark gray. Adult snakes are usually about 2 1/2 feet in length.

Agkistrodon contortrix pictigaster — **TRANS-PECOS COPPERHEAD** (Fig. 89 a, b, c)

DESCRIPTION:
 The Trans-Pecos copperhead closely resembles the Broadbanded copperhead in that it has straight-edged crossbands; although it differs from

130

all the other forms in that it has a uniformly dark ventral area. The crossbands on the back of the snake have narrow, dark borders. The ground color is a light hazel brown. The Trans-Pecos copperhead does not attain a length of much over 2 feet and is confined primarily to far West Texas.

Agkistrodon piscivorus leucostoma — **WESTERN COTTONMOUTH MOCCASIN**
(Fig. 90 a, b, c, d, e)

DESCRIPTION:

This heavy, large, semi-aquatic snake is one of the most dangerous snakes found in the state. It is often confused with other non-venomous water snakes of the genus *Natrix*. The head of the Cottonmouth is triangular-shaped and relatively flat. Great variation in ground color is seen within this species. Adults usually have a background of dark brown and are marked with 10 - 15 irregularly edged crossbands. On some specimens the crossbands are clearly defined while others show little or no pattern. General coloration varies from black to olive green with the lower jaw being lighter than the top of the head. Juvenile forms are vividly marked with dark brown bands edged with white against a gray background. The Cottonmouth derives its name from the white oral mucosa which is seen when the snake opens its mouth.

GENERAL COMMENTS:

In attempting to identify a snake, particularly the rattlers, the presence of the rattle is the first thing that should be looked for. All rattlesnakes, no matter what their age, will have some semblance of a rattle. In the event the rattle has been forcibly removed, the tail will appear quite stubby and sawed off.

The fangs of all three of these genera protrude from the maxilla and measure approximately 1/2 inch in length. Both fangs are very mobile and are erect during the act of striking. Because of the curvature of the fang, the opening of the jaw must be maintained close to 180° in order to provide a perpendicular angle to the surface to achieve any effective penetration (Fig. 91). At rest, the fang is encased in a sheath of tissue and is folded back against the palate. Most species of these snakes have several reserve fangs which quickly replace broken or extruded ones.

The venom apparatus is a modified salivary gland, and the adult snake carries from 0.75 - 1.5 ml. of venom in the sac (Fig. 92). The control of the amount of venom injected at each bite is accomplished through the musculature surrounding the venomous apparatus, with an average of only 11% of the venom in the sac being extruded at any one time. It is rare that more than 1/2 of the sac contents will be injected. Such variability in the

131

amount of venom injected is exemplified by the clinical findings - that in probably 15 - 30% of the snakebite victims, no actual envenomation occurs (4).

TOXICOLOGY AND PATHOPHYSIOLOGY:

It is difficult to classify snake venoms simply as neurotoxic, shock-producing, or hematoxic and hemorrhagic because of the heterogenous composition of the venoms. On the other hand, they can exert primary toxic and lethal effects upon hemopoietic, cardiovascular, respiratory, or nervous systems depending upon the specific venom considered. Although the exact components of the *Crotalidae* venom remain unknown, some fractions have been isolated and studied in detail. Those include phospholipase A, hyaluronidase, proteinases, ribonuclease, desoxyribonuclease, phosphodiesterase, and ATPase. The lethal fractions, however, appear to be more closely related to non-enzymatic components. On the other hand, both the pathophysiologic effects and the toxicity of the venom seem to relate, at least experimentally, to the individual enzymes. The clinical findings of tissue necrosis, hemolysis, the reactive vasomotor instability, and complete disruption of endothelial lining of the capillaries characteristically encountered in patients with rattlesnake envenomation are attributable to the actions of phospholipase A. In addition, phospholipase A is found to attack the cell membrane resulting in membrane disruption and disintegration of fibrinogen.

Hyaluronidase, the spreading factor, can hydrolyze the hyaluronic acid gel of the tissue matrix, and such breakdown of tissue matrix will allow other enzymatic fractions of the venom to penetrate further into the tissue space, thus further enhancing the damaging effects. Proteinases, which are trypsin-like enzymes, cause tissue damage by digesting tissue proteins. The anticoagulant effect of the snake venom is similarly believed to be due to the proteolytic disintegration of fibrinogen.

The enzymatic activities are further accentuated by the presence of phosphodiesterase which is thought to be responsible for retardation and inhibition of the high energy ATP resynthesis. The presence of ATPase, ribonuclease, and desoxyribonuclease, although the exact roles of these enzymes remain ill-defined, can conceivably enhance the deleterious effects of phosphodiesterase. The combined action of these enzymes is believed to account for the shock phenomenon frequently associated with the snakebite (1, 8, 16).

The pathophysiologic effects of pit viper venoms are complex and multifold. The usual clinical findings of continuous oozing and bleeding from the operative site, profound anemia, profuse tissue hemorrhage with subsequent necrosis, and shock are due not only to the derangement in the clotting mechanisms induced by the snake venom but are also due to the morphological changes in the erythrocytes, the thrombocytes, and the blood vessels (3, 12). One of the most outstanding changes induced by the pit viper venom occurs in the hemopoietic system, specifically in the erythrocytes. The appearance of the erythrocyte is altered from its normal biconcave disc to that resembling a mulberry. The change has been termed a "burring" phenomenon (Figs. 93, 94). The "burring" phenomenon has been found both in experimental animals as well as in patients following envenomation. Since such morphological change of the erythrocyte can be induced by a trace amount of pit viper venom, it is considered to be a useful sign in qualitating snake envenomation. It is also observed that the elasticity and the rigidity of the erythrocyte's cell membrane are altered, and with time, a complete disintegration of the cell eventually ensues. In addition to the loss of erythrocytes into the tissue space due to the injuries occurring in the endothelial lining of the capillaries, a massive destruction of the red blood cells accounts for the anemia seen in patients with a severe degree of envenomation.

Coagulatory derangements evidenced by the findings of continuous oozing and bleeding from the fang marks or wound edges following either an incision or an excisional therapy, occur in patients suffering from envenomation (Fig. 95). The extent of derangement appears to depend upon the amount of venom injected. In a recent study, it was shown that the coagulatory defects induced by rattlesnake venom involves the entire spectrum of clotting factors (5). These abnormalities and the changes in the red blood cell morphology, in conjunction with the loss of the structural integrity of the capillaries, leading to loss of intravascualr fluids into tissue spaces, may be the prime factors responsible for the pathogenesis of the hypovolemic shock frequently associated with severe rattlesnake envenomation. Primary toxic effects of the pit viper venom upon the heart and the central nervous system, though present, are limited. Cardiac and neural dysfunctions which may be observed in patients are probably the results of hemorrhagic diathesis involving these vital structures.

SYMPTOMATOLOGY:

The clinical manifestations produced by a pit viper's envenomation locally, include initial pain which may be extremely intense, followed by local swelling which progresses with time (Fig. 96 a, b, c, d). On the other hand, pain may be minimal or completely absent in severe poisoning. Erythema and ecchymosis develop as subcutaneous hemorrhage occurs. These changes, in conjunction with the findings of fang marks are considered invaluable in the diagnosis of snakebite (Fig. 97). As time passes, paresthesia and hypesthesia with some degree of local anesthesia may occur in the immediate area of the bite. A grading system for the severity of the pit viper bite has been advocated for the purpose of providing a therapeutic guide.

133

The severity of envenomation is classified according to the magnitude of systemic manifestations and is divided into 4 grades (13).

Grade I   Minimal envenomation: Usually no general symptoms or systemic involvement. Fang or tooth marks are apparent. Moderate to severe pain is present. Edema and erythema ranging from 1 - 5 inches in diameter is present during the initial 12 hours.

Grade II   Moderate envenomation: Systemic involvement possible with general symptoms including lowgrade fever, some signs of neurotoxicity, nausea, vomiting, giddiness, shock, and palpable lymph nodes. Severe local pain is present. Edema and erythema ranging from 6 - 12 inches is present during the initial 12 hours.

Grade III Severe envenomation: Systemic involvement frequently present with general symptoms including rapid, thready pulse, hypothermia, ecchymoses, and generalized petechiae. Shock may rapidly follow the injury. Severe pain is present with edema and erythema spreading to an area greater than 12 inches.

Grade IV   Extremely severe envenomation: Systemic involvement apparent with symptoms including blood-tinged secretions, renal shutdown, coma, and death. Multiple fang marks are frequently present. Edema is widespread and may include the trunk ipsilateral to the involved extremity.

The use of this grading system has certain pitfalls and is in no way absolute. With the passage of time clinical manifestations often change thus necessitating regrading of the symptoms.

Unlike the tissue swelling which can be diffuse, the extent of hemorrhagic changes within the tissue is a practical guide in determining the magnitude of the local spread of the venom. A complete removal of these hemorrhagic tissues, therefore, is essential when an excisional therapy is used in the management of the patient. Extravasation of the intravascular fluids rich in protein and blood components is thought to be the factor responsible for the pathogenesis of edematous swelling of the involved area. Excessive swelling of the tissue in a closed compartment, such as the extremities, on occasion may compromise the circulation. Such circulatory embarassment, usually manifested as pain, numbness, and cyanosis, should be watched for closely. Should symptoms appear, proper measures must be taken in order to avoid any disastrous consequences of ischemia (Fig. 100 a, b).

A continuous oozing and bleeding from the fang marks and wound edges from incision or excision is another common finding (Fig. 95). In extreme cases, such steady and continuous loss of fluid may account for a subsequent hypovolemia.

Systemic manifestations produced by envenomation are variable depending upon the amount of venom injected. The clinical signs and symptoms due to fright, commonly manifested as dyspnea, semiconsciousness, cold and clammy skin, feeble pulse, nausea, and vomiting are oftentimes difficult to distinguish from those due to the actual systemic poisoning. On the other hand, the findings of an hemoptysis, hemoglobinuria, and the failure of the blood to clot in a test tube or around the wound site, and findings of the "burring" phenomena (Fig. 94) clearly indicate an envenomation of a significant magnitude. With more extensive envenomation, toxic delirium associated with convulsions, coma, and death can occur in extreme cases.

Secondary complications of tissue necrosis, particularly around the area of the bite, are quite common in patients who have survived the initial crisis. The necrosis of the tissue often can be so extensive that an amputation of the extremity or extensive debridement followed by a secondary reconstruction of deformities may become necessary.

TREATMENT:

First Aid: First aid in the case of a snakebite, as in other forms of medical emergencies, can be life-saving. People bitten by snakes often become excited, hysterical, and panicky whether the bite is inflicted by a harmless or a venomous species. The symptoms due to fright may become so serious that such behavior actually hinders in rendering necessary first aid. The following procedures should be followed in the case of a snakebite:

(1) Identify the snake; (2) Look for fang marks if the snake is recognized as a poisonous species; (3) Immobilize the involved part; (4) A light (lymphatic) tourniquet should be applied to the area above the site of the bite; (5) Cleanse the area thoroughly with water, alcohol, or antiseptic solution. An incision, to include the fang marks, may be made on the envenomation site. The incision, however must not exceed 1/2 inch in length, nor more than 1/4 inch in depth. Suction may be performed by the use of the suction cups or by mouth. It should be continued for at least 30 minutes. If the time elapsed exceeds 15 - 20 minutes, such an approach is usually of no value. (6) Intermittent hypothermia, for short periods of time (25 - 30 minutes), should be produced by packing the injured site with ice or ice bags. The involved area should not be submerged in ice water. Care must be taken in producing the hypothermia since any extended period of time may produce severe frostbite.

Excisional Therapy: This method of treatment is based on the finding that the bulk of the venom remains in the area of the bite for a period of time following envenomation. A major portion of the venom can be removed by excising the envenomated tissue (6, 7).

The area involved must be first cleansed with a copious amount of irrigating fluid to eliminate residual venom adhering to the skin surface.

135

Remove the tourniquet prior to the operative procedure. The area is frequently anesthetic and may not require the use of a local anesthetic. However, if it is necessary, the skin can be infiltrated with local anesthetics along the lines of incisions. The margin of ecchymosis rather than the area of swelling and edema is used to determine the exact extent of excision. A skin flap should be fashioned and an entire thickness of the subcutaneous tissue should be removed (Fig. 98 a, b, c, d). If construction of a skin flap is difficult, the skin and subcutaneous tissue may be excised and defatted skin can be used as a full thickness skin graft. Effort must be made to remove as much hemorrhagic tissue as possible from area. Care must be taken to avoid injury to nerves, large vessels, and tendons if it involves the extremities.

Wound Management Following Excision: The defects may be covered by defatted skin as a full thickness skin graft immediately if the elevation of the skin flap is impractical (Fig. 99 a, b, c, d, e, f). If the oozing from the area of excision is excessive, the wound may be packed with iodoform gauze and a partial thickness skin graft applied at a later date. The skin graft can be obtained by means of a free hand skin knife, razor dermatome, or other portable dermatomes. The graft should be immobilized by means of stents.

Ancillary Treatment: Contamination of the venom by various organisms is definitely a possible threat, and the proper measures should be taken to prevent such a complication. All patients should be immunized against tetanus actively and/or passively. Broad spectrum antibiotics should be administered by the intravenous route during the first 24 to 48 hours (10).

In rare occasions, patients can show the signs and symptoms of allergic reaction, not only to the antivenin administered, but also to the snake venom. Large doses of steroids, e.g. Solu-Medrol 4 to 6 gm. may be used to combat such complications. Species specific antivenin or the Wyeth Polyvalent Crotalidae Antivenin (18) is used if the general condition of the patient is rapidly deteriorating.

Hemorrhagic diathesis is a common complication following a pit viper bite with all the clotting factors being affected by the venom. Although the process usually reverses within 24 to 48 hours, bleeding diathesis can involve the gastrointestinal tract, respiratory tract, and/or the urinary tract. Since the laboratory studies in such instance will indicate poor progression of the clotting factor regeneration, a transfusion with fresh blood may become necessary. Blood obtained from an immediate relative with the same blood type is preferred. The results are quite dramatic.

The patient should not be allowed to take anything orally for the first 24 to 48 hours due to the possibility of nausea and vomiting. An analgesic should be prescribed to assure the comfort of the patient.

Laboratory Studies: Upon arrival at the hospital, the following laboratory studies should be ordered: (1) complete blood count, (2) prothrombin time,

(3) plasma fibrinogen level, (4) platelet count, and (5) partial prothrombin time. These studies should be repeated every 4 to 6 hours during the first day and daily thereafter during the remaining hospital stay. An adequate intravenous route should be maintained for the purpose of blood replacement as well as medications. Four to 6 units of fresh blood should be kept ready. Additional ancilliary laboratory studies such as plasma protein electrophoresis, plasma electrolytes levels, and urinalysis can be ordered at regular time intervals for the clinical assessment of the patient's status.

Antivenin: (Fig. 101) The use of antivenin in the management of the poisonous snakebite has been the mainstay of conventional medical treatment. The intravenous administration of antivenin is usually recommended for the bite of the snakes in the *Crotalus, Sistrurus,* and *Agkistrodon* genera. A polyvalent antivenin for use against the pit viper venom is available from the Wyeth Laboratories (18). It must be remembered, however, that the antivenom is prepared by hyperimmunizing horses and proper measures in ruling out a possible hypersensitivity reaction to the horse serum should be taken prior to the injection. It should also be remembered that a skin test, which is usually used in testing for hypersensitivity, is not reliable in the presence of shock. The recommended dose of Wyeth Polyvalent Crotalidae Antivenin according to various grades of manifestation is as follows: mild degree of envenomation (Grade I by classification of McCullough): 1 vial; moderate degree of envenomation (Grade II): 2 to 4 vials; severe grade of envenomation (Grade III): 5 to 10 vials; extremely severe grade of envenomation (Grade IV): 10 to 20 or more vials (13, 19).

GENUS — *MICRURUS*

Micrurus fulvius tenere — **TEXAS CORAL SNAKE** (Fig. 102 a, b, c, d)

DESCRIPTION:
This small snake has a characteristic pattern consisting of red, yellow, and black rings that encircle the body in regular order. A broad black ring is followed by a much narrower yellow ring. Next is a broad red ring which has black pigment scattered throughout it. The use of the tricolor pattern in distinguishing the Coral snake from other similarly colored non-venomous forms is responsible for the familiar admonition: "Red on yellow, kill a fellow; red on black, venom lack." In the Coral snake the red and yellow rings are always touching. The nose is black and a yellow band falls across the top of the head, which is small and narrow.

The fangs, unlike those of the pit vipers, occur as 1 or more pairs and are short, rigid, immovable, and deeply grooved and are located at the very end of the upper jaw. The coral snake averages less than 2 1/2 feet in length and has a body diameter of about 3/8 inch.

GENERAL COMMENTS:

While this colorful snake is shy, nonagressive and generally has an inoffensive nature, its venom makes it the most deadly of all Texas snakes. Envenomation is usually the result of careless handling of the snake. Because of the size and rigidity of the fangs as well as the limited jaw excursion, this snake must move around to achieve an effective bite. Also, a chewing motion is required to accomplish the injection of the venom. Coral snake bites occur very infrequently and are responsible for only 1 - 2% of the persons treated for snakebite (14).

TOXICOLOGY AND PATHOPHYSIOLOGY:

It is the consensus that the venom from the phylogenetically older snakes, such as a member of the family *Elapidae,* differs profoundly from newer snakes in the family *Crotalidae.* The venom of the Coral snake is considerably more poisonous and is recognized to be primarily neurotoxic. However, the enzymes phospholipase A, hyaluronidase, proteinase, ribonuclease, desoxyribonuclease, and phosphodiesterase constitute the major components of the venom found in this snake. Therefore, hemolysis, disruption of the endothelial lining of the capillaries, hemorrhage and tissue necrosis, the erythrocyte "burring" phenomena (Figs. 93, 94), and reactive vasomotor reaction are also encountered in patients bitten by the Coral snake. Enzymes such as cholinesterase and acid and alkaline phosphatase have also been isolated from the venom of members of this family. The exact significance of these enzymes, however, remains obscure.

Neurotoxicity of the Coral snake venom is characterized by central nervous system depression, vasomotor instability, and muscle paralysis. The "neurotoxins" isolated from the family *Elapidae* are primarily those of basic polypeptides. However, the exact components of these "neurotoxins" vary from species to species. It is known that a curare-like blockage of neuromuscular transmission is the primary factor responsible for the muscular paralysis that causes the commonly encountered respiratory failure. The onset of neurotoxic blockage at the neuromuscular junction, compared to that induced by d-tubocurarine, is much slower, and is less reversible once the blockage is established (11).

SYMPTOMATOLOGY:

The findings immediately after the bite of the Coral snake is that of one or more tiny puncture wounds in the area of envenomation. Pain is usually minimal and the amount of swelling around the site of the bite is insignificant. The wound often resembles that of superficial scratch marks. The systemic manifestations of the poisoning are often delayed, and the complaints of apprehension, giddiness, nausea, vomiting, excess salivation, and even a sense of euphoria are quite common. These symptoms may appear 1 to 7 hours after the bite. The signs of neurotoxicity are those of a bulbar-type, manifested as cranial motor nerve paralysis involving the eyelids, extrinsic musculature of the eyeball, and paralysis of respiratory muscles. This cranial nerve paralysis is clinically manifested as diplopia, blurring vision, and impairment of the respiratory movements. Hematologic toxicity induced by the coral snake venom, though less extensive, is similar to the pit viper venom. The findings of ecchymosis, the tissue necrosis around the area of envenomation, changes in the morphology of the red blood cell (the "burring" phenomena), and the hemolysis with deranged clotting mechanisms are seen occasionally.

The main cause of death in patients bitten by the Coral snake is due to respiratory failure. The sensorium of the patients on the other hand is clear as long as the respiratory movements are maintained by mechanical means (14).

TREATMENT:

First Aid: An immediate immobilization of the involved part is essential in minimizing the active spreading, diffusion, and absorption of the venom. Cleansing of the skin surface by means of copious irrigation around the area of the bite is important due to the fact that residual venom on the skin surface may gain access to the open wound. As first aid treatment, a light lymphatic tourniquet should be applied above the sight of the injury and the limb immobilized. Ice bags, if available, may be used to pack around the site of the bite until the patient is transported to the hospital.

Antivenin: (Fig. 103) The intravenous use of antivenin is strongly recommended in the case of Coral snake bite since the primary action of the venom is that of neurotoxicity. Clinical manifestations may only be prevented by use of a specific antivenin. Currently, the Coral Snake Antivenin is available either directly from Wyeth Laboratories (18) or from the Communicable Disease Center, Atlanta, Georgia (2). This antivenin is produced by hyperimmunizing horses against the venom of the North American Coral Snake, *Fulvius,* and will protect against the venom of the Eastern Coral Snakes and the Texas Coral Snakes. Dosage recommended for Coral snake specific antivenin is as follows: mild to moderate degree of envenomation: 2 to 8 vials; severe degree of envenomation: 8 to 12 vials. The dose can be repeated every 4 to 6 hours until the victim recovers. The exact amount of antivenin used, in actual practice, is governed by the severity of envenomation and the clinical manifestations. The Wyeth Laboratories Polyvalent Crotalidae Antivenin and Polyvalent Cobra Antivenin are not effective against the coral snake bite and should not be used.

Excisional Therapy: The area of envenomation must be first cleansed with a copious amount of irrigating fluid to remove the residual venom which may be left on the skin surface. The skin is infiltrated with a local anesthetic along the line of incisions. The extent of hemorrhage in the tissue is less extensive as compared to envenomation by pit vipers. However, it is advisable to fashion the skin flap in such a manner that envenomated tissue can be removed totally. Care must be taken to avoid the injuries to nerves, vessels, and tendon structures if the site of involvement is in the extremity.

Wound Management Following Excision: The skin flap may be resutured following defatting. A small drain is placed in the wound and a pressure dressing should be applied. On the other hand, if the wound is extensive, a delayed skin grafting is preferred, and the area can be covered by using a partial thickness skin graft.

Ancilliary Treatment: Contamination of the venom by various organisms is definitely a possible threat to the patient. Proper measures should be taken to prevent such complications. All patients should be immunized against tetanus, either actively and/or passively. A broad spectrum antibiotic should be used for a period of 7 to 10 days. In a small number of patients, an allergic reaction to the snake venom as well as to the administered antivenin may occur. Large doses of steroids, e.g. Solu-Medrol 4 to 6 gm., may be used to combat this complication. Unlike pit viper envenomation, hemorrhagic diathesis is uncommon. The use of fresh blood transfusions should be considered if persistent oozing and bleeding from the site of the wound is evident. The signs of the neurotoxicity manifested clinically as diplopia, ptosis of the eyelids, and difficulty in breathing may appear several hours following the accident. The use of a volume ventilator should be considered mandatory if signs and symptoms of respiratory failure become apparent. A continuous monitoring of the blood gases is essential during this period of time in order to ascertain the adequacy of oxygen exchange.

VENOMOUS SNAKES

REFERENCES

1. Christy, N. P. "Poisoning by Venomous Animals". *Amer. J. Med.* 42:107 (1967).

2. Communicable Disease Center, Atlanta, Ga.

3. Denson, K. W. E. "Coagulant and Anticoagulant Action of Snake Venoms". *Toxicon.* 7:5 (1969).

4. Gennaro, J. F. "Observations on the Treatment of Snakebite in North America" in *Venomous and Poisonous Animals and Noxious Plants of the Pacific Region.* H. L. Keegan, Editor, The MacMillan Co., New York, 1963, p. 427.

5. Huang, T. T., S. R. Lewis and T. Bond. Unpublished Data.

6. Huang, T. T., J. B. Lynch and S. R. Lewis. "Experimental Studies in Snakebite Treatment". Presented at the Plastic Surgical Research Council Meeting, Boston, 1972.

7. Huang, T. T., J. B. Lynch, D. L. Larson and S. R. Lewis. "The Use of Excisional Therapy in the Management of Snakebite". *Ann. Surg.* 179:598 (1974).

8. Jimenez-Porras, J. M. "Biochemistry of Snake Venoms". *Clin. Toxicol.* 3:389 (1970).

9. Klauber, L. M. *Rattlesnakes, Their Habits, Life Histories, and Influence on Mankind.* Vol. 1. Univ. of California Press, Berkeley, 1956, p. 13.

10. Ledbetter, E. O. and A. E. Kutscher. "The Aerobic and Anaerobic Flora of Rattlesnake Fangs and Venom. Therapeutic Complications". *Arch. Environ. Health.* 19:770 (1969).

11. Lee, C. Y. "Elapid Neurotoxins and their Mode of Action". *Clin. Toxicol.* 3:457 (1970).

12. Malette, W. G., J. B. Fitzgerald, A. T. K. Cockett, T. G. Glass, W. G. Glenn and P. V. Donnelly. "The Pathophysiologic Effects of Rattlesnake Venom (Crotalus atrox)" in *Venomous and Poisonous Animals and Noxious Plants of the Pacific Region.* H. L. Keegan, Editor, The MacMillan Co., New York, 1963, p. 339.

13. McCollough, N. C. and J. F. Gennaro. "Evaluation of Venomous Snake in Southern United States from Parallel Clinical and Laboratory Investigations". *J. Florida Med. Ass.* 49:959 (1963).

14. Parrish, H. *M.* "Bites by Coral Snakes: Report of 11 Representative Cases". *Amer. J. Med. Sci.* 253:561 (1967).

15. Parrish, H. M. "Texas Snakebite Statistics". *Texas State J. Med.* 60:592 (1964).

16. Russel, F. E. and H. W. Puffer. "Pharmacology of Snake Venoms". *Clin. Toxicol.* 3:433 (1970).

17. Stebbins, R. C. *A Field Guide to Western Reptiles and Amphibians.* Houghton Mifflin Company, Boston, 1966, p. 186.

18. Wyeth Laboratories. P. O. Box 8299, Philadelphia, Pa. 19101.

19. Wyeth Laboratories. "Directions for Use of Antivenin (Crotalidae) Polyvalent". Circular 2145, Rev. 3/19/65.

SNAKES

GENERAL BIBLIOGRAPHY

1. Conant, R. *A Field Guide to Reptiles and Amphibians of Eastern North America.* Houghton Mifflin Co., Boston, 1958.

2. Stebbins, R. C. *A Field Guide to Western Reptiles and Amphibians.* Houghton Mifflin Co., Boston, 1966.

3. Werler, J. E. *Poisonous Snakes of Texas and First Aid Treatment of Their Bites,* Bulletin No. 31, Texas Parks and Wildlife Dept., Austin, 1950.

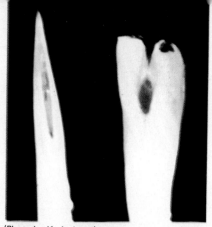

Fig. 74. PIT VIPER FANG

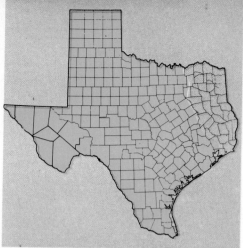

Fig. 75 a. WESTERN DIAMONDBACK RATTLESNAKE - Distribution *(Crotalus atrox)*

Fig. 75 b. WESTERN DIAMONDBACK RATTLESNAKE *(Crotalus atrox)*

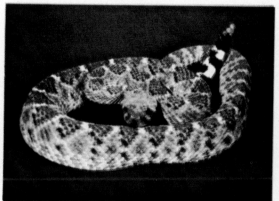

Fig. 75 c. WESTERN DIAMONDBACK RATTLESNAKE (Light Phase)

Fig. 75 d. WESTERN DIAMONDBACK RATTLESNAKE - JUST PRIOR TO SHEDDING ITS SKIN.

(Modified From, Texas Parks & Wildlife Dept., Bull. No. 31)
Fig. 76 a. TIMBER RATTLESNAKE
Distribution *(Crotalus horridus horridus)*

Fig. 76 b. TIMBER RATTLESNAKE *(Crotalus horridus horridus)*

(Photo by K. A. Jones)
Fig. 77 a. CANEBRAKE RATTLESNAKE
(Crotalus h. atricaudatus)

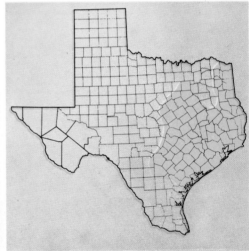

(Modified From, Texas Parks & Wildlife Dept., Bull. No. 31)
Fig. 77 b. CANEBRAKE RATTLESNAKE
- Distribution *(Crotalus h. atricaudatus)*

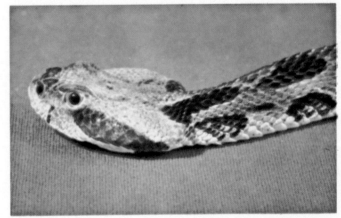

Fig. 77 c. CANEBRAKE
RATTLESNAKE *(Crotalus h. atricaudatus)*

Fig. 78 a. MOTTLED ROCK RATTLESNAKE
(Crotalus lepidus lepidus)

Fig. 78 b. MOTTLED ROCK
RATTLESNAKE

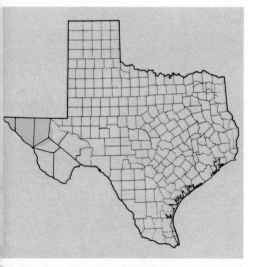

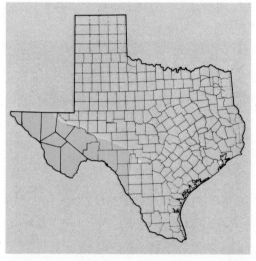

(Modified From, Texas Parks & Wildlife Dept., Bull. No. 31)

Fig. 78 c. MOTTLED ROCK
RATTLESNAKE - Distribution

(Modified From, Texas Parks & Wildlife Dept., Bull. No. 31)

Fig. 79 a. BANDED ROCK RATTLESNAKE
- Distribution

Fig. 79 b. BANDED ROCK RATTLESNAKE
(Crotalus I. klauberi)

Fig. 79 c. BANDED ROCK
RATTLESNAKE
(Crotalus I. klauberi)

Fig. 80 a. NORTHERN BLACKTAILED RATTLESNAKE*(Crotalus molossus)*

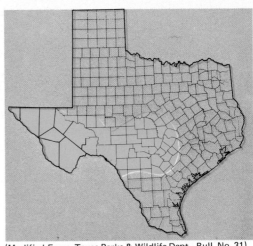

(Modified From, Texas Parks & Wildlife Dept., Bull. No. 31)
Fig. 80 b. NORTHERN BLACKTAILED RATTLESNAKE - Distribution *(Crotalus molossus)*

(Photo by K. A. Jones)

Fig. 81 a. PRAIRIE RATTLESNAKE *(Crotalus viridis viridis)*

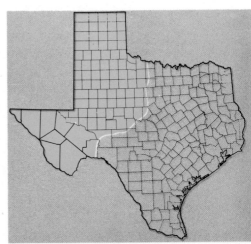

(Modified From, Texas Parks & Wildlife Dept., Bull. No. 31)
Fig. 81 b. PRAIRIE RATTLESNAKE - Distribution *(Crotalus viridis viridis)*

Fig. 82 a. MOJAVE RATTLESNAKE *(Crotalus scutulatus scutulatus)*

Fig. 82 b. MOJAVE RATTLESNAKE
(Crotalus scutulatus scutulatus)

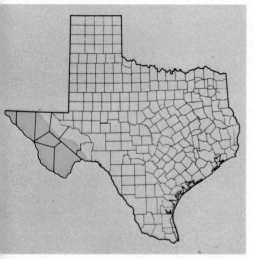

Modified From, Texas Parks & Wildlife Dept., Bull. No. 31)
Fig. 82 c. MOJAVE RATTLESNAKE-
Distribution *(Crotalus scutulatus scutulatus)*

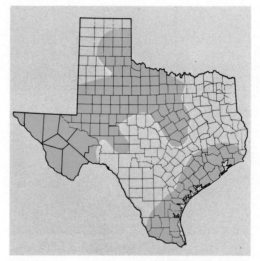

(Modified From, Texas Parks & Wildlife Dept., Bull. No. 31)
Fig. 83 a. WESTERN MASSASAUGA-
Distribution *(Sistrurus catenatus tergeminus)*

Photo by K. A. Jones)
Fig. 83 b. WESTERN MASSASAUGA
Sistrurus catenatus tergeminus)

Fig. 83 c. WESTERN MASSASAUGA
(Sistrurus catenatus tergeminus)

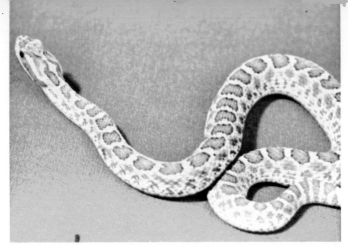

Fig. 84 a. DESERT MASSASAUGA
(Sistrurus catenatus edwardsi)

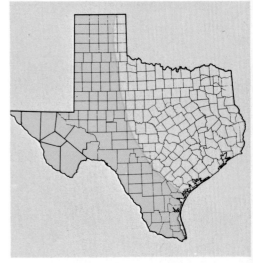

Fig. 84 b. DESERT MASSASAUGA- Distribution *(Sistrurus catenatus edwardsi)*

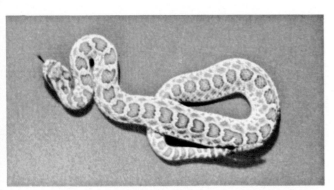

Fig. 84 c. DESERT MASSASAUGA
(Sistrurus catenatus edwardsi)

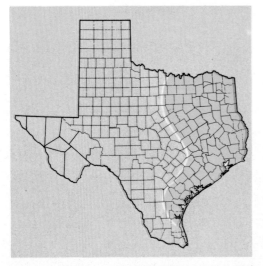

(Modified From, Texas Parks & Wildlife Dept., Bull. No. 31)

Fig. 85 a. WESTERN PIGMY RATTLESNAKE - Distribution *(Sistrurus miliarius streckeri)*

(Photo by K. A. Jones)

Fig. 85 b. WESTERN PIGMY RATTLESNAKE *(Sistrurus miliarius streckeri)*

Fig. 86 a. SOUTHERN COPPERHEAD
(Agkistrodon contortrix contortrix)

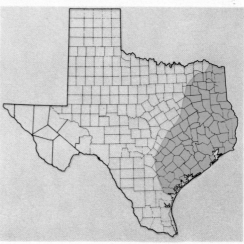

(Modified From, Texas Parks & Wildlife Dept., Bull. No. 31)

Fig. 86 b. SOUTHERN COPPERHEAD -
Distribution *(Agkistrodon c. contortrix)*

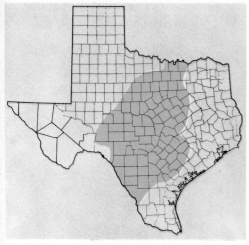

(Modified From, Texas Parks & Wildlife Dept., Bull. No. 31)
Fig. 87 a. BROADBANDED COPPERHEAD
Distribution *(Agkistrodon c. laticinctus)*

Fig. 87 b. BROADBANDED COPPERHEAD
(Agkistrodon contortrix laticinctus)

Fig. 88 a. NORTHERN COPPERHEAD
(Agkistrodon contortrix mokasen)

(From, Texas Parks & Wildlife Dept., Bull. No. 31)

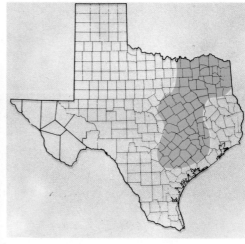

(Modified From, Texas Parks & Wildlife Dept., Bull. No. 31)
Fig. 88 b. NORTHERN COPPERHEAD
Distribution *(Agkistrodon c. mokasen)*

Fig. 89 a. TRANS-PECOS COPPERHEAD
(Agkistrodon contortrix pictigaster)

Fig. 89 b. TRANS-PECOS COPPERHEAD
(Agkistrodon c. pictigaster)

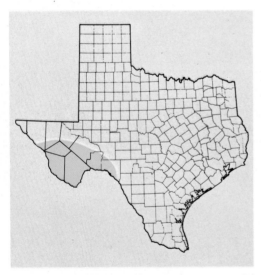

(Modified From, Texas Parks & Wildlife Dept., Bull. No. 31)

Fig. 89 c. TRANS-PECOS COPPERHEAD -
Distribution (Agkistrodon c. pictigaster)

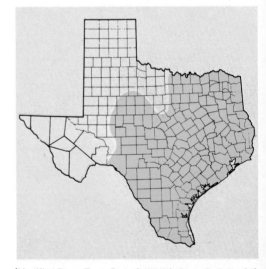

(Modified From, Texas Parks & Wildlife Dept., Bull. No. 31)

Fig. 90 a. WESTERN COTTONMOUTH
MOCCASIN - Distribution (Agkistrodon
piscivorous leucostoma)

Fig. 90 b. WESTERN COTTONMOUTH
MOCCASIN (JUVENILE - Dorsal view)
(Agkistrodon p. leucostoma)

Fig. 90 c. WESTERN COTTONMOUTH
MOCCASIN (JUVENILE - Ventral view)
(Agkistrodon p. leucostoma)

Fig. 90 d. WESTERN COTTON-
MOUTH MOCCASIN (JUVENILE)
(Agkistrodon p. leucostoma)

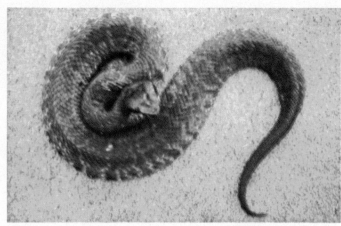

(Photo by K. A. Jones)

Fig. 90 e. WESTERN COTTONMOUTH MOCCASIN
(ADULT) *(Agkistrodon piscivorous leucostoma)*

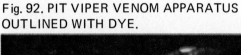

Fig. 92. PIT VIPER VENOM APPARATUS
OUTLINED WITH DYE.

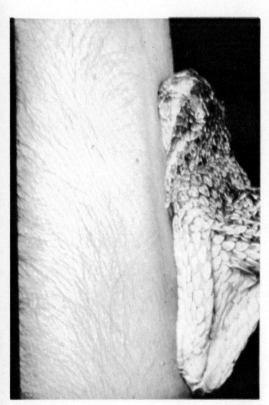

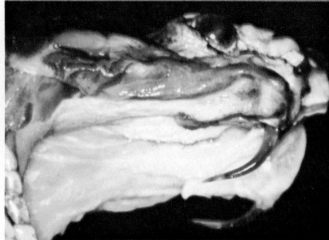

(Photo by K. A. Jones)

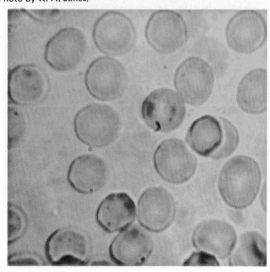

(Photo by K. A. Jones)

Fig. 91. THE PIT VIPER MOUTH OPENS
180° WHEN STRIKING.

Fig. 93. NORMAL RED BLOOD CELL.

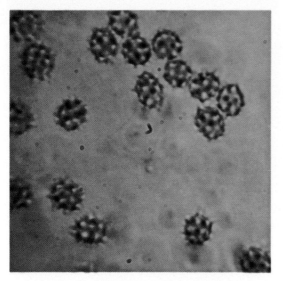

Fig. 94. "BURRING" PHENOMENON

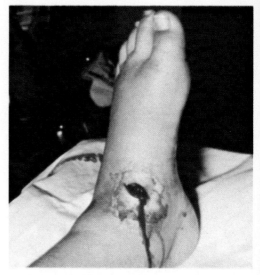

Fig. 95. CONTINUOUS OOZING OF INCISION FOLLOWING ENVENOMATION.

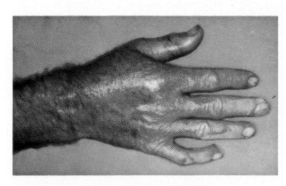

Fig. 96 a. 1 HOUR AFTER SNAKEBITE.

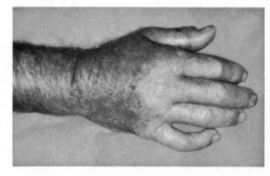

Fig. 96 b. 6 HOURS AFTER SNAKEBITE.

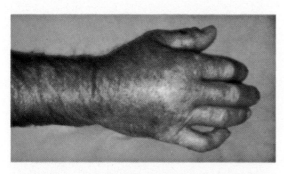

Fig. 96 c. 12 HOURS AFTER SNAKEBITE.

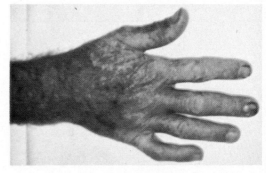

Fig. 96 d. 3 DAYS AFTER SNAKEBITE.

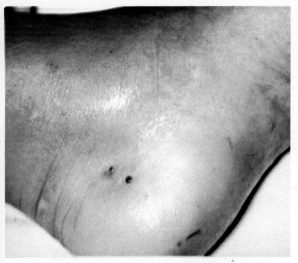

Fig. 97. FANG MARKS AND ECCHYMOSIS.

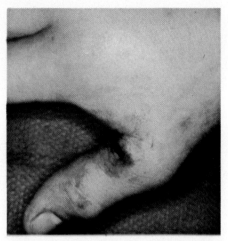

Fig. 98 a. SNAKEBITE INVOLVING THE THUMB.

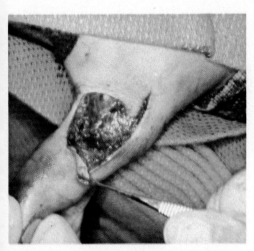

Fig. 98 b. SKIN FLAP FASHIONED.

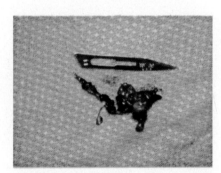

Fig. 98 c. HEMMORRHAGIC TISSUE REMOVED.

Fig. 98 d. 2 MONTHS AFTER SNAKEBITE.

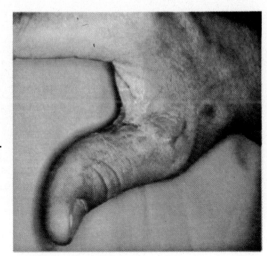

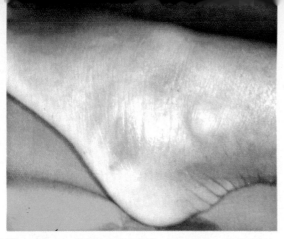

Fig. 99 a. ECCHYMOSIS AFTER COTTON-MOUTH MOCCASIN BITE.

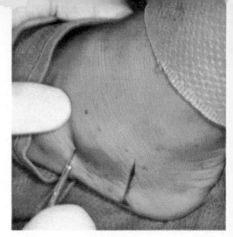

Fig. 99 b. INCISIONS ARE MADE.

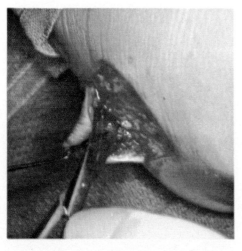

Fig. 99 c. THE SKIN IS REMOVED.

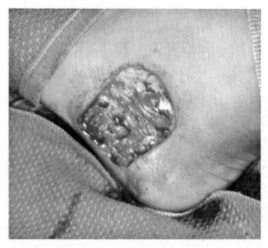

Fig. 99 d. A FULL LAYER OF SUBCUTANEOUS TISSUE IS REMOVED.

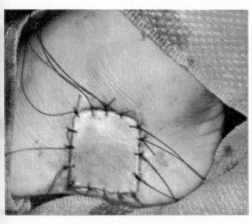

Fig. 99 e. SKIN GRAFTED WITH DEFATTED SKIN.

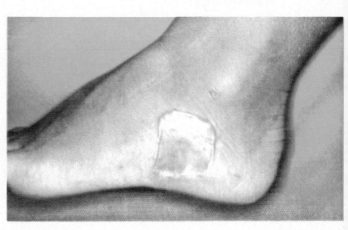

Fig. 99 f. 2 MONTHS AFTER THE SNAKEBITE.

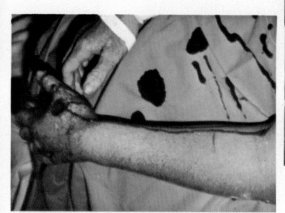

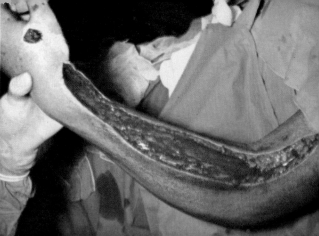

Fig. 100 b. FASCIOTOMY IS REQUIRED TO RELIEVE THE VASCULAR INTER-FERENCE FROM TISSUE SWELLING.

Fig. 100 a. EXCESSIVE SWELLING OF THE TISSUE INTERFERES WITH CIRCULATION IN THE HAND.

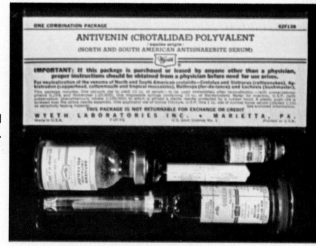

Fig. 101. POLYVALENT ANTIVENIN FOR PIT VIPER ENVENOMATION.

Fig. 102 a. TEXAS CORAL SNAKE *(Micrurus) fulvius tenere)*

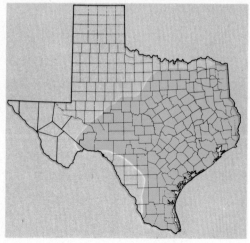

(Modified From, Texas Parks & Wildlife Dept., Bull. No. 31)

Fig. 102 b. TEXAS CORAL SNAKE Distribution *(Micrurus f. tenere)*

Fig. 102 c. TEXAS CORAL SNAKE *(Micrurus fulvius tenere)*

(From, Texas Parks & Wildlife Dept., Bull. No. 31)

Fig. 102 d. TEXAS CORAL SNAKE (Left); MEXICAN MILK SNAKE (Right).

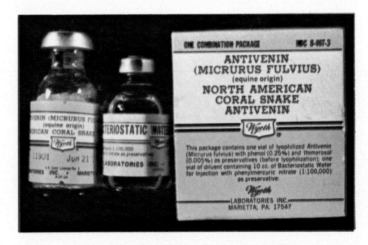

Fig. 103. CORAL SNAKE ANTIVENIN.

NON - VENOMOUS TEXAS SNAKES

Fig. 104. WESTERN COACHWHIP *(Masticophis flagellum glagellum)*

(Photo by E. J. Morris)

Fig. 105. TEXAS SCARLET SNAKE *(Cemophora coccinea lineri)*

(Photo by K. A. Jones)

Fig. 106. PRAIRIE KINGSNAKE *(Lampropeltis calligaster calligaster)*

(Photo by E. J. Morris)

Fig. 107. WESTERN PATCH-NOSED SNAKE *(Salvadora hexaleris)*

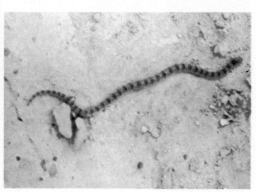

(Photo by E. J. Morris)

Fig. 108 a. WESTERN HOOK-NOSED SNAKE *(Ficimia cana)*

(Photo by E. J. Morris)

Fig. 108 b. WESTERN HOOK-NOSED SNAKE *(Ficimia cana)*

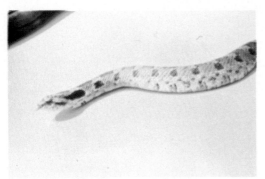

(Photo by K. A. Jones)

Fig. 109. WESTERN HOGNOSE SNAKE (JUVENILE) *(Heterodon nasicus)*

Fig. 110 a. EASTERN HOGNOSE SNAKE (JUVENILE) *(Heterodon platyrhinos)*

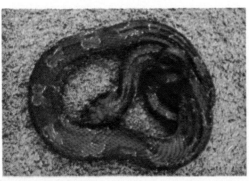

(Photo by K. A. Jones)

Fig. 110 b. EASTERN HOGNOSE SNAKE (ADULT) *(Heterodon platyrhinos)*

(Photo by E. J. Morris)

Fig. 110 c. EASTERN HOGNOSE SNAKE (ADULT) *(Heterodon platyrhinos)*

Fig. 111 a. TRANS-PECOS KINGSNAKE (LIGHT PHASE) *(Lampropeltis m. blairi)*

Fig. 111 b. TRANS-PECOS KINGSNAKE (DARK PHASE) *(Lampropeltis m. blairi)*

NON - VENOMOUS TEXAS SNAKES

Fig. 112. TEXAS INDIGO SNAKE
(Drymarchon corais erebennus)

Fig. 113. TRANS-PECOS RAT SNAKE
(Elaphe subocularis)

Fig. 114. SONORA KINGSNAKE
(Lampropeltis getulus)

Fig. 115. TEXAS LONGNOSED SNAKE
(Rhinocheilus l. tessallatus)

(Photo by K. A. Jones)

Fig. 116. SPECKLED KINGSNAKE
(Lampropeltis getulus holbrooki)

Fig. 117. SMOOTH GREEN SNAKE
(Opheodrys vernalis)

Fig. 118 a. TEXAS BROWN SNAKE (DEKAY'S SNAKE) *(Storeria dekayi texana)*

Fig. 118 b. TEXAS BROWN SNAKE (DEKAY'S SNAKE) *(Storeria dekayi texana)*

(Photo by E. J. Morris)

Fig. 119. TEXAS GLOSSY SNAKE *(Arizona elegans elegans)*

Fig. 120. SONORA GOPHER SNAKE *(Pituophis melanoleucus affinis)*

(Photo by E. J. Morris)

Fig. 121. MEXICAN BLACK - HEADED SNAKE *(Tantilla planiceps atriceps)*

(Photo by T. G. Hulsey)

Fig. 122. WESTERN MUD SNAKE *(Farancia abacura reinwardti)*

(Photo by E. J. Morris)

Fig. 123. BANDED WATER SNAKE *(Natrix sipedon faciata)*

Fig. 124. GREAT PLAINS RAT SNAKE *(Elaphe guttata emoryi)*

Fig. 125. LOUISIANA PINE SNAKE *(Pituophis melanoleucus ruthveni)*

Fig. 126. BULL SNAKE (LIGHT PHASE) *(Pituophis melanoleucus sayi)*

Fig. 127 a. MEXICAN MILK SNAKE *(Lampropeltis triangulum annulata)*

Fig. 127 b. MEXICAN MILK SNAKE *(Lampropeltis triangulum annulata)*

(Photo by E. J. Morris)

Fig. 128 a. SPOTTED NIGHT SNAKE (DARK PHASE) *(Hypsiglena torquata ochrorhyncha)*

Fig. 128 b. SPOTTED NIGHT SNAKE (LIGHT PHASE) *(Hypsiglena torquata ochrorhyncha)*

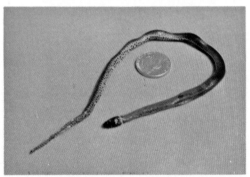

(Photo by K. A. Jones)

Fig. 129. REGAL RINGNECKED SNAKE *(Diadophis p. regalis)*

(Photo by E. J. Morris)

Fig. 130. RINGNECKED SNAKE *(Diadophis punctatus)*

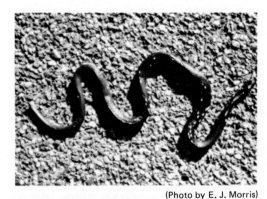

(Photo by E. J. Morris)

Fig. 131. BUTTERMILK SNAKE *(Coluber constructor anthicus)*

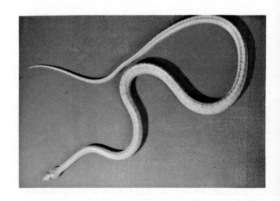

Fig. 132. BAIRD'S RAT SNAKE *(Elaphe obsoleta bairdi)*

(Photo by K. A. Jones)

Fig. 133. ROUGH EARTH SNAKE *(Haldea triatula)*

(Photo by E. J. Morris)

Fig. 134. TEXAS RAT SNAKE *(Elaphe obsoleta lindheimeri)*

Fig. 135 a. YELLOW-BELLIED WATER SNAKE *(Natrix erythrogaster flavigaster)*

(Photo by K. A. Jones)

Fig. 135 b. YELLOW-BELLIED WATER SNAKE *(Natrix erythrogaster flavigaster)*

(Photo by K. A. Jones)

Fig. 135 c. YELLOW-BELLIED WATER SNAKE *(Natrix e. flavigaster)*

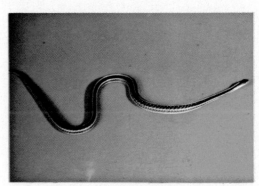

Fig. 136. TEXAS GARTER SNAKE *(Thamnophis sirtalis annectens)*

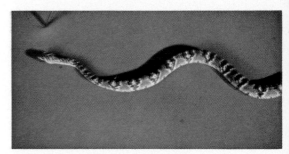

Fig. 137 b. TEXAS LYRE SNAKE
(Trimorphodon vilkinsoni)

Fig. 137 a. TEXAS LYRE SNAKE
(Trimorphodon vilkinsoni)

The Texas Lyre Snake has fangs in the rear of its mouth and is capable of injecting venom if it is allowed to strike. The venom, however, is only minimally toxic and requires little more than local treatment.

DANGEROUS
ARTHROPODS

DANGEROUS ARTHROPODS

Don W. Micks, Sc.D.

INTRODUCTION

Insects and other arthropods which have been associated with human illness and death as the result of allergic stings, venomous bites, contact toxins, invasion of human tissues, *et cetera,* are far too numerous to mention in this particular compilation. Individual (human) variation coupled with differences in the quantity and quality of allergen or venom introduced accounts for the wide range of reactions which for the most part tend to be of a local nature, but may proceed to acute illness and death, with or without anaphylaxis.

The examples chosen for this section are among the most medically important species encountered by physicians and their patients. Many of these species or related ones are present throughout the United States. Furthermore, since the treatment is essentially the same for allergic reactions following stings of bees, wasps, hornets, ants, certain caterpillars, and scorpions (except in Arizona and surrounding areas where an antivenin is available for a poisonous species) the exact identity of the offending species is helpful but not prerequisite to effective symptomatic treatment. Nevertheless, the arthropod involved in the sting or bite should be collected and taken in for identification whenever possible.

The black widow spider and the brown spiders of the genus *Loxosceles* are singled out for special attention inasmuch as they are relatively common, and envenomations due to these species are troublesome to treat if not life-threatening. It should be emphasized however, that numerous other kinds of spiders possess venom and are capable of producing an irritating bite. Most of these are infrequently involved in such human contacts.

Latrodectus mactans — **BLACK WIDOW SPIDER, HOUR-GLASS SPIDER**
(Fig. 140)

DESCRIPTION:

The adult female, which is responsible for most bites, is approximately 1 1/2 inches long (legs extended), glossy black in color with a red or orange hour-glass marking on the ventral side of the abdomen.

GENERAL:

The female spider is found with her web and egg sacs in protected places, *i.e.,* under stones, logs, long grass, brush piles, barns, garages, privies, *et cetera.* The bite frequently occurs when the web is disturbed, and may not be felt. There may or may not be a local lesion with two tiny red spots representing the penetration of the chelicerae (fangs). Bites most often occur on the extremities.

SYMPTOMATOLOGY:

Initially there may be pain at the site of the bite which lasts for an hour or two. Subsequently, depending upon the area bitten, local muscular cramps occur and may involve the thigh, shoulder or back. The pain characteristically spreads to the abdomen where the muscles assume a board-like rigidity. Tightness in the chest, difficulty in breathing, nausea, vomiting, and sweating are frequently present.

TREATMENT:

Once the diagnosis of black widow spider bite is made, the patient should receive the specific antivenin (Black Widow Spider Antivenin) (17). The contents of one vial are administered intramuscularly *after* the tests for serum sensitivity (directions enclosed with vial) are made (1). Symptoms usually subside in 1 - 3 hours. The intravenous injection of 10 ml. of 10% calcium gluconate can also be given for the control of muscle pain. Muscle relaxants have been used with success where calcium therapy did not provide pain relief.

Loxosceles reclusa — **BROWN RECLUSE, BROWN SPIDER, FIDDLE-BACK SPIDER** (Fig. 138 a, b)

DESCRIPTION:

The brown recluse is a small brown spider that grows to about the size of a half-dollar (including the legs). It is easily identified by the violin-shaped or fiddle-shaped marking on the cephalothorax (back).

GENERAL:

Typically brown spider bites occur in little used storage areas such as cellars and closets, or while putting on clothing which is seldom used. The bite involves the penetration of the skin by the chelicerae (fangs) and may or may not be felt. Although the bite frequently occurs on the extremities, it may involve any part of the body. The venom, which has not been completely characterized, produces local necrosis. (Fig. 139 a, b, c, d, e)

SYMPTOMATOLOGY:

In the majority of cases, signs and symptoms are confined to the general site of the bite, and may be initiated by slight itching or localized pain. The area becomes red, swollen, and tender, often within 10 hours, and a small bleb or blister is generally present. A black eschar (scab) develops which sloughs after several days, leaving a draining, sharply-demarcated ulcer with a base of granulation tissue. The ulcer varies in diameter from a few millimeters to several centimeters (typically dime-size) and heals slowly (4).

In some cases, chills, fever, nausea and vomiting have occurred, especially in children. Occasionally a faint rash may be seen over the body and extremities. Rarely, hemolysis and death have been associated with the bite of this species.

TREATMENT:

Since there is no specific antivenin for *Loxosceles reclusa* bites, management must necessarily be of a symptomatic nature and is still somewhat controversial. A number of physicians have reported that acute manifestations responded well to early (6 - 8 hours post-bite) and vigorous treatment with systemic corticosteroids (7), and that in some instances necrosis did not occur.

The lesion is usually refractory to antihistamines, antibiotics, and other agents which have been used topically as well as systemically. Early total excision when it appears that necrosis is inevitable, has been used with success in some cases followed by split thickness skin grafting (5, 7, 14).

Megalopyge opercularis — **PUSS CATERPILLAR, TREE ASP** (Fig. 142)

DESCRIPTION:

This beige-to-gray or chocolate-colored caterpillar is the larval stage of a small beige moth. When the caterpillar matures it is approximately 1 inch long and is covered with fine hair-like projections. On the back of this animal intermingled with the fine hairs, are clusters of venomous spines.

GENERAL:

The tree asp is frequently abundant during October and November, but may also be present during the spring months, when it is found eating the leaves of a variety of trees and bushes. It is commonly found on exterior walls of houses, fences, gates, *et cetera,* where contact with the caterpillar is likely to occur.

SYMPTOMATOLOGY:

Classically, there is a severe burning sensation immediately after the sting, followed rapidly by acute stabbing pain which radiates to the adjacent axillary or inguinal region within approximately 10 minutes of the sting. Lymphadenitis is commonly present. Typically, the site is erythematous with some edema. Dermatitis which occurs at the sting site may persist for a number of days, often in a grid-like pattern (9).

TREATMENT:

The application of ice immediately after the sting often reduces the pain at the site. Antihistamines have been administered intramuscularly and by mouth with moderate success in some cases (10). Calcium gluconate may provide rather rapid and dramatic relief from pain. Its use should be considered for those patients in whom ice does not satisfactorily reduce local pain (9, 11). Analgesics may also be used where indicated.

Centruroides vittatus — COMMON STRIPED SCORPION (Fig. 141)

DESCRIPTION:

The striped scorpion seldom attains a length greater than 3 inches. Its body is tan to dark brown with reddish stripes running the length of the body.

GENERAL:

Scorpions are typically nocturnal in their habits, hiding either in damp, cool areas, *i.e.,* under rocks and logs outside, or in cracks and crevices inside dwellings where they may get into shoes or other clothing. Children tend to be stung more frequently than adults. Venom is injected into the victim by a stinger in the tip of the tail. The puncture made by the sting may or may not be visible.

SYMPTOMATOLOGY:

Centruroides vittatus is a comparatively innocuous species, the sting of which is usually followed by a sharp pain or burning sensation followed by a wheal that soon disappears with no complications. Swelling and discoloration may or may not be present.

173

TREATMENT:

Treatment is ordinarily not required, except for *Centruroides sculpturatus* (16) which is largely confined to Arizona and surrounding area. Ice may be applied to the sting area for the relief of symptoms and an antihistamine should be administered.

HYMENOPTERA — STINGING INSECTS

Apis mellifera   —   **HONEY BEE** (Fig. 143)

Bombus spp.   —   **BUMBLE BEE** (Fig. 144)

Polistes spp.   —   **PAPER WASP, YELLOW JACKET** (Fig. 145)

Solenopsis spp.   —   **FIRE ANT** (Fig. 146 a, b)

DESCRIPTION:

Apis mellifera - **HONEY BEE** - This small winged insect attains a length of about 1/2 inch and is frequently found in meadows and around flower gardens and lawns. This bee is honey-colored or golden with black or dark brown stripes that encircle the body of the insect.

Bombus spp. - **BUMBLE BEE** - This winged insect is usually about 1 inch in length and is yellow and black in color. The bumble bee is responsible for much fewer stings than the honeybee. The nest of this insect is a wax comb that is built in the ground or in hollow logs.

Polistes spp. - **PAPER WASP, YELLOW JACKET** - This yellow and brown striped flying insect usually attains a length of about 1 inch. Many stings have resulted from this relatively aggressive insect. Its nest consists of flat paper combs usually built under the eves of buildings or in bushes or trees. Several species of *Polistes* are abundant in Texas, and the coloring may range from solid red to solid black.

Solenopsis spp. - **FIRE ANT** - These ants are usually red in color with dark brown to black posterior segments. Two pincers are attached to the head of this ant and they aid in grasping the victim so that several stings can be inflicted with its stinger, located on the posterior portion of the insect's body. One member of this species, *Solenopsis saevissima richteri,* the imported fire ant, produces the most severe sting of this group. Stings usually occur when the mound of this ant is disturbed. The mound is usually about 18 inches in diameter and 10 - 12 inches high (3, 15).

GENERAL:

There is no doubt that hymenopterous insects constitute a much greater medical problem in Texas (as well as other states) than all other arthropods combined (12). They are winged (except for the ants) and possess stinging organs which are projected from the posterior end of the abdomen introducing venom or allergen through the skin. Bees and wasps may fly away after stinging the victim before they can be recognized or identified. However, ants are usually present on the skin during the initial stinging sensation. The stinger of wasps and ants may be used repeatedly, but the honey bee is the only species which leaves its stinger and associated venom sac attached to the skin.

SYMPTOMATOLOGY:

In the majority of persons stung by hymenopterous insects, the reaction is only local. There may be redness, itching, swelling, formation of a wheal or pain at the site. The local swelling may be extensive causing discomfort, fear, and apprehension (8). Symptoms may persist for several hours but will gradually resolve, with or without medication. The next sting, however, may cause severe systemic or even fatal results (12).

Probably less than 5% of the population experiences severe systemic reactions following stings, apparently due to an allergic reaction. The usual manifestations are urticaria, asthma, rhinitis, headache, malaise, abdominal cramps, and shock, and may proceed to fatal anaphylaxis (2).

TREATMENT:

In the case of an actual or suspected bee sting, the stinger should be located and carefully scraped off the skin. Forceps should not be used to remove the stinger since the squeezing of the venom sac (which is attached to the stinger) will inject more venom into the patient. An ice pack should be applied locally to the sting site. The administration of an antihistamine and/or ephedrine hydrochloride will provide some relief when the symptoms are mild. With more severe symptoms, epinephrine hydrochloride should be administered subcutaneously at once and repeated in 15 to 30 minutes if necessary (8). The insect sting-sensitive patient should always have an emergency kit available. The kit should contain a preloaded sterile syringe of epinephrine hydrochloride 1:1,000 or an epinephrine inhaler, a tourniquet, and an antihistamine (13). When the sting occurs on an extremity, a tourniquet should be applied to retard circulation of the antigen. An antihistamine, such as chlorpheniramine (10 mg) or diphenhydramine (50 mg) may be administered parenterally. Aminophylline (250 - 500 mg) may be administered slowly intravenously for bronchospasm (8). Oxygen, respiratory support, and even tracheostomy for laryngeal obstruction should be available for use if required. Corticosteroid therapy should be reserved for those cases that fail to respond to the above measures. Hyposensitization is

175

indicated for any patient who has had a generalized reaction to insect stings (6, 8). This usually consists of weekly subcutaneous injections of an extract containing equal parts of bee, hornet, and wasp whole body extracts, gradually increasing from a weak to a stronger extract.

ARTHROPOD

REFERENCES

1. Arena, J. *Poisoning.* 2nd Ed., Charles C. Thomas, Springfield, Ill., 1970, pp. 454-456.

2. Barnard, H. B. "Nonfatal Results in Third-degree Anaphylaxis from Hymenoptera Stings". *J. Allergy* 45:92-96 (1969).

3. Brown, L. L. "Fire Ant Allergy". *So. Med. J.* 65:273-277. (1972).

4. Duffey, P. H. and H. P. Limbacher. "Brown Spider Bites in Arizona". *Ariz. Med.* 28:89-95 (1971).

5. Fardon, D. W., C. W. Wingo, D. W. Robinson, and F. W. Masters. "The Treatment of Brown Spider Bite". *Plast. Reconstr. Surg.* 40:482-488 (1967).

6. Henderson, L. L. "Acute Reaction to Insect Sting". *Postgrad. Med.* 49:191-193 (1971).

7. Hershey, F. B. and C. E. Aulenbacher. "Surgical Treatment of Brown Spider Bites". *Ann. Surg.* 170:300-308 (1969).

8. Levine, M. I. "Insect Stings". *J. A. M. A.* 217:964. (1971).

9. McGovern, J. P., G. D. Barkin, T. R. McElhenney and R. W. Wende. "Megalopyge opercularis". *J. A. M. A.* 175:121-124 (1961).

10. McMillam, C. W. and W. R. Purcell. "Hazards to Health - The Puss Caterpillar, Alias Wooly Slug". *New Eng. J. Med.* 271:147-149 (1964).

11. Micks, D. W. "Clinical Effects of the Sting of the 'Puss Caterpillar' *(Megalopyge opercularis* S. & A.) on Man". *Texas Rep. Biol. Med.* 10:399-405 (1952).

12. Micks, D. W. "Insects and Other Arthropods of Medical Importance in Texas". *Texas Rep. Biol. Med.* 18:624-635 (1960).

13. Passerro, M. A. and S. C. Dees. "Allergy to Stings from Winged Things". *Amer. Fam. Physician* 7:74-79 (1973).

14. Reed, H. B., R. H. Hackman and F. M. Fesmire. "Variation in Severity of Loxoscelism". *J. Tenn. Med. Ass.* 61:1097-1102 (1968).

15. Smith, J. D. and E. B. Smith. "Multiple Fire Ant Stings". *Arch. Derm.* 103:438-441 (1971).

16. Stahnke, H. L. and J. Stahnke. "Treatment of Scorpion Sting". *Ariz. Med.* 14:576 (1957).

17. Wyeth Laboratories. P. O. Box 8299, Philadelphia, Pa. 19101.

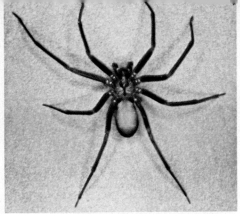

(Photo by P. N. Morgan)

Fig. 138 a. BROWN RECLUSE SPIDER (FEMALE) *(Loxosceles reclusa)* (x2)

(Photo by P. N. Morgan)

Fig. 138 b. BROWN RECLUSE SPIDER (MALE) *(Loxosceles reclusa)* (x2)

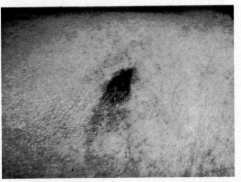

Photo by P. N. Morgan)

Fig. 139 a. 4-6 HOURS AFTER BITE.

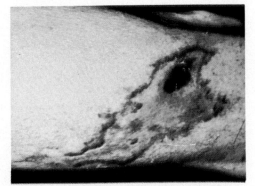

(Photo by P. N. Morgan)

Fig. 139 b. ABOUT 3 DAYS AFTER BITE.

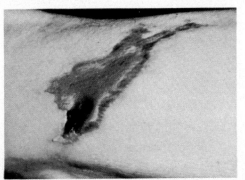

(Photo by P. N. Morgan)

Fig. 139 c. ABOUT 2 WEEKS AFTER BITE.

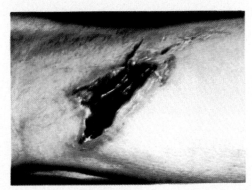

(Photo by P. N. Morgan)

Fig. 139 d. ABOUT 6 WEEKS AFTER BITE.

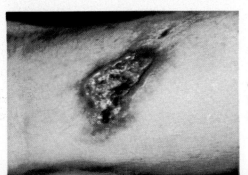

(Photo by P. N. Morgan)

Fig. 139 e. ABOUT 4 MONTHS AFTER BITE.

Fig. 140. BLACK WIDOW SPIDER (FEMALE) (VENTRAL SIDE) *(Latrodectus mactans)* (x3)

(Photo by P. N. Morgan)

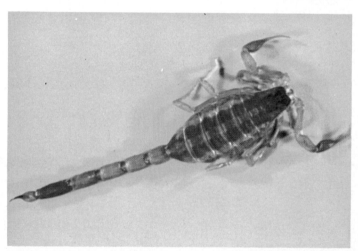

Fig. 141. COMMON STRIPED SCORPION *(Centruroides vittatus)* (x2)

(Photo by C. A. Long)

Fig. 142. PUSS CATERPILLAR, TREE ASP *(Megalopyge opercularis)*

(Photo by A. Campos)

Fig. 143. HONEY BEE *(Apis mellifera)*

Fig. 144. BUMBLE BEE *(Bombus sp.)*

Fig. 145. PAPER WASP, YELLOW JACKET *(Polistes sp.)*

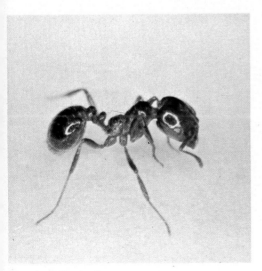

Fig. 146 a. FIRE ANT *(Solenopsis sp.)* (x7)

Fig. 146 b. FIRE ANT MOUND.

DANGEROUS
MARINE LIFE

DANGEROUS MARINE LIFE

H. G. Love, Jr., M.D.
Linda L. Stephens, M.S.

187

INTRODUCTION

The ocean waters are inhabited by a large variety and number of marine creatures that are dangerous to humans by virtue of either their ability to bite, lacerate, or sting, or due to their containing toxic substances within their flesh, blood, *et cetera.* The region defined for the selection of this harmful marine life encompasses the inland estuarine and seashore environment to the open seas of the waters of North America.

It is hoped that with the use of the photographs and descriptions of these creatures, their ready identification will be possible, thus allowing for speedy and efficient medical treatment of any injury they might produce. Line drawings (Figures 147–149) are included to aid the reader in utilizing the individual descriptions of the different marine organisms. All size measurements are indications of length, except where noted. The symptoms and treatment that are characteristic for each type of emergency produced by one of these creatures are designed to guide either the physician or paramedic in the therapeutic procedures indicated.

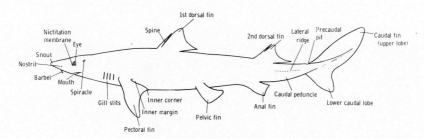

Fig. 147. SHARKS

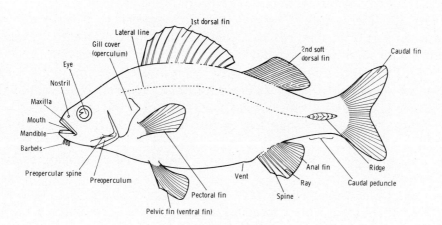

Fig. 148. BONY FISHES

189

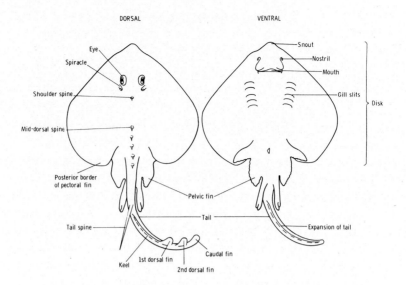

Fig. 149. SKATES AND RAYS

The following definitions from Russell (56) are useful to the physician or paramedic confronted with the evaluation and emergency treatment of an injury, envenomation, or poisoning from marine life in the Gulf of Mexico.

Definitions:

Injurious Marine Life: Applied to those marine creatures who inflict traumatic wounds to a human without the injection of a poison or a venom. These wounds can vary from trivial to life threatening.

Venomous Marine Life: Usually applied to those creatures which are capable of producing a toxin in a highly developed secretory organ or group of cells and which can deliver this toxin during an act of biting or stinging.

Poisonous Marine Life: These animals are regarded as those whose tissues, either in part or in their entirety, are toxic to humans. In reality, all venomous animals are poisonous, but not all poisonous animals are venomous.

Fish Poisoning is synonymous with Ichthyotoxism. It does not include that type of poisoning which may occur following ingestion of fish contaminated by bacterial pathogens, which is designated as scombroid poisoning.

Halstead in 1964 divided Ichythyotoxic fishes into three (3) subdivisions (27).

1. Ichthyosarcotoxic Fishes: contain a toxin in their musculature, viscera or skin.
   Example: CIGUATERA
2. Ichthyootoxic Fishes: produce a toxin generally confined to the gonads and roe.
3. Ichthyohemotoxic Fishes: the toxin is solely in the blood of the fish.

190

Dr. Halstead's classification is both academic and practical in that it assists the attending physician or paramedic in accurately completing his medical records and in reporting to public health authorities.

All suspected or potentially harmful species have not been included here due to insufficient incriminating reports of human toxicity on exposure to them. However, in cases of questionable toxicity, envenomation, injury, or poisoning, one or two representative species of suspected genera have been discussed.

SEA URCHINS

Arbacia punctulata	—	**PURPLE SEA URCHIN, COMMON ATLANTIC SEA URCHIN** (Fig. 150)
Diadema antillarum	—	**BLACK SEA URCHIN, NEEDLE-SPINED URCHIN, SEA NEEDLE, SEA EGG** (Fig. 151)
Lytechinus variegatus	—	**WHITE SEA URCHIN** (Fig. 152)
Tripneustes ventricosus	—	**SEA EGG, SEA URCHIN** (Fig. 153)

DESCRIPTION:

Arbacia punctulata - **PURPLE SEA URCHIN** - The brittle, dome-shaped shell of the purple sea urchin is hidden under a covering of 1 - 3 inch spines. The upper spines are pointed while the lower ones have spatulate tips. It may be either red, brown, or purple to almost black in color. Its range includes the rocky bottoms at moderate depths of 225 meters to seaweeds in tidal pools.

Diadema antillarum - **BLACK SEA URCHIN** - The body of this sea urchin is a slightly flattened sphere measuring 6 inches across with many very long (10 inches) spines radiating from the body wall. It is usually very dark brown or black around the shell. The spines of juveniles typically are alternately banded purple and white, while the central body is black with occasional spots of deep blue.

This light-sensitive species may be found during the day burrowed into rock crevices or clustered in congregations of 3 - 12 in cavities of coral reefs. During the night, it may be conspicuously found upon rocks or corals or on the sandy ocean floor.

Lytechinus variegatus - **WHITE SEA URCHIN** - The white sea urchin is characterized by many moveable solid white spines which radiate from a good-sized, central, flattened, darkly colored shell. This urchin is a bottom dweller, is very sluggish in habit, and is found both intertidally and in deeper waters.

Tripneustes ventricosus - **SEA EGG** - This sea urchin has many moveable spines used in locomotion, that radiate out from the central dome-like shell. This urchin is a bottom form and are usually found bored into hard substrata near a reef.

GENERAL:

Many varieties of sea urchins appear in the Gulf of Mexico. Some are considered to be not only injurious but venomous. Those which are both injurious and venomous include the sea egg *(Tripneustes ventricosus)*, the white sea urchin *(Lytechinus variegatus)*, and the black sea urchin *(Diadema antillarum)*.

SYMPTOMATOLOGY:

The penetration of the skin by the sea urchin's needle-sharp spines may produce an immediate and intense burning sensation. The pain is soon followed by redness, swelling, and an aching sensation. Numbness and muscular paralysis have been reported. Secondary infections are not uncommon.

TREATMENT:

Attention is directed to the need for prompt removal of the embedded spines from the skin if it does not involve extensive surgical exercise. The majority of these calcium carbonate foreign bodies will be extruded from the skin beneath a small pustule in a period of about three days. They are extremely difficult to remove even under magnification with very delicate surgical instruments as they are very brittle and break off easily. The discoloration of the area around the wounds is due to the purple dye that is secreted by the animal. This should not be disturbing since it is apparently harmless. The wounds should be rinsed with alcohol. Hot water soaks should be used for a period of 1 hour. The wounded area can be left exposed to the air and then observed frequently for either the extrusion or absorption of the embedded spines or any sign of wound complication. Ordinarily the patient does not require either a tetanus booster or the administration of broad spectrum antibiotics. Signs and symptoms of systemic intoxication are treated symptomatically. Supportive care should be provided. (1, 8, 23, 24, 26, 46, 47, 48, 51, 55, 56, 59, 60).

Eunice sp. — POLYCHAETE WORM (Fig. 154 a, b)

DESCRIPTION:

The polychaete worm is characterized by a smooth soft body with longitudinal divisions of the body wall forming a series of segments. This worm has reduced bristle-like locomotory appendages along the body wall. Anteriorly, this creature possesses a powerful jaw apparatus containing two pharyngeal teeth, as well as many cuticular teeth capable of inflicting severe bites. The polychaete worm is found hunting for food in rock crevices and is encountered upon turning over small rocks on reefs.

SYMPTOLOLOGY:

The bite of this worm is typically one that is triangular in shape, due to the contour of its biting mouth parts. It produces both severe pain and intense swelling in a short period of time. Even following immediate definitive therapy, the area of the wound may itch for a considerable number of days following the injury.

TREATMENT:

The treatment is warm saline soaks, the administration of broad spectrum antibiotics, tetanus toxoid booster, and inspection of the wound at frequent intervals for any signs of wound complication, foreign body reaction, or infection including anaerobic granulomatous lesions produced by *Mycobacterium marinum* (23, 24, 47, 48, 63).

Gonodactylus bredini — **MANTIS SHRIMP** (Fig. 155 a, b)

DESCRIPTION:

This shrimp resembles a minute lobster; having the same sturdy, cylindrical body with shield-like body covering and muscular abdomen ending in a fan-shaped tail that can be cupped quickly for backward locomotion. In addition, there are several pairs of thoracic appendages which serve as walking legs. A second pair of legs are highly specialized jack-knife claws capable of inflicting serious wounds. In addition to these jack-knife claws, many sharp spines project beyond the edge of the sturdy tail fin. The tail fin is translucent and colored with yellow markings on the appendages. This shrimp may reach 8 inches in length. The mantis shrimp is predatory in habit, lurking in small holes in the sea floor, particularly where the water is less than 100 feet deep', although it is often found in lagoons.

SYMPTOMATOLOGY:

The lacerations produced by the front claws and/or tail of the mantis shrimp may be quite severe. Although this species is relatively small, it has been known to attack anyone bothering it. Uninformed individuals who have tried to remove this shrimp from a cast net have received numerous deep cuts on the hand. Of special interest to divers, an attacking mantis shrimp have been known to produce a crack in a face mask!

TREATMENT:

Treatment of these lacerations should be handled routinely like any other traumatic wound. However, since these wounds are highly infective and contaminated, they should be irrigated with copious quantities of an antibiotic or saline solution. The patient should receive a tetanus toxoid booster and a broad spectrum antibiotic. The wound requires frequent observation for any signs of wound complication, foreign body reaction, or infection including anaerobic granulomatous lesions produced by *Mycobacterium marinum* (26, 47, 48, 61, 62, 63).

195

Lolliguncula brevis — **BRIEF SQUID** (Fig. 156)

Octopus vulgaris — **COMMON OCTOPUS** (Figs. 157, 158, 159)

DESCRIPTION:
> *Lolliguncula brevis* - **BRIEF SQUID** - This small, shiny, soft-bodied, cylindrical invertebrate form has 8 short arms, 2 longer arm-like tentacles; and a short, rounded caudal fin. The jaws form a beak that is effective in defense. The eyes are large and are located immediately posterior to the arms. An internal stiff "bone", or pen serves to give both support and form to this mollusk. Squid have been captured up to nine inches in length. Its width is less than half its length. It is an active nocturnal form, inhabiting bays and inlets.

> *Octopus vulgaris* - **COMMON OCTOPUS** - This warty-skinned octopus is capable of readily changing color and is characterized by 8 sucker-studded arms, which reach a length of 3 feet, radiating from a dome-like head that is equipped with 2 eyes and a beaked mouth. The well-developed eyes are an important part of its defense, as is its capability to release ink. It attains a length of about 24 inches. It is a native of the warmer estuarine waters and is often found hiding out in lairs among the rocks of jetties and sea walls, open bays, and inlet areas. It can attain a weight of 20 - 40 pounds.

GENERAL:
> Since the octopus and the squid belong to the same general family, they will be discussed under the same heading. Some species of octopus and squid are venomous. The particular octopus that occupies the Gulf of Mexico is venomous. Octopus bites, although infrequent, consist of two small puncture wounds which are produced by the sharp, parrot-like jaws.

SYMPTOMATOLOGY:
> A burning or tingling sensation is the usual initial symptom. At first the discomfort is localized but may later encompass the entire appendage. Bleeding is frequently profuse for the size of the bite which may indicate that the clotting process of the blood is retarded. Swelling, redness, and heat commonly develop in the area about the wound. Recovery is generally uneventful.

> One fatality from an octopus bite, however, is reported in the literature. This incident took place near Darwin, Australia, when a diver captured a small octopus of unknown species which had a span of only about 20 centimeters. The diver permitted the octopus to crawl over his arms and shoulders and finally to the back of his neck where the animal bit him. A few minutes after the bite the victim complained of a sensation of dryness in his mouth and of difficulty in swallowing. After walking a short distance up

the beach from the scene of the accident, he began to vomit, developed a loss of muscular control, finally suffered from respiratory distress, and was unable to speak. He was rushed to a hospital and given respiratory assistance, but expired in about two hours.

TREATMENT:

Wounds of the bites of the octopus and squid should be treated by immersing the part in tap water, as hot as can be tolerated, for a period of about one hour in order to neutralize the venom. The wounds can then be treated in a conservative manner by mild debridement, irrigation, and coverage with an antibiotic and a bulky pressure dressing. The wound should be inspected frequently for any signs and symptoms of wound complications, foreign body reaction, or infection including anaerobic granulomatous lesions produced by *Mycobacterium marinum.* The patient should be given both broad spectrum antibiotics and a tetanus toxoid booster. Signs and symptoms of systemic intoxication are treated symptomatically. Supportive care should be rendered (42, 47, 48, 51, 52, 55, 56, 59, 60, 63).

MORAY EELS

Gymnothorax funebris   —   **GREEN MORAY** (Fig. 160)

Gymnothorax moringa   —   **COMMON SPOTTED MORAY EEL, SPOTTED MORAY** (Fig. 161)

Gymnothorax nigromarginatus   —   **BLACK-EDGE MORAY EEL** (Fig. 162)

DESCRIPTION:

Gymnothorax funebris - **GREEN MORAY** - The jaws of this eel-like fish contain numerous sharp teeth and characteristically do not completely close. Its color is dark olive brown, nearly plain or paler on the throat, sometimes with very faint darker marblings. The dorsal and anal fins are marked with longitudinal dark lines. The belly is without transverse markings. The mucous that is secreted by this vertebrate is yellow when scraped from the body. This is a warm water inhabitant defending a position in rock crevices on reefs. It can attain a length of up to 6 feet.

Gymnothorax moringa - **SPOTTED MORAY** - The eel-like body of this fish is elongate and rounded, more or less compressed, and covered with a layer of mucus. The dorsal and anal fins are continuous with the caudal fin. There are confluent round spots on the body which serve to reduce the pale ground

197

color to narrow reticulations on a surface of black. The dorsal and anal fins are similarly spotted. The narrow margin of the anal fin is yellow. The jaws of the spotted moray contain many sharp teeth and are capable of inflicting serious lacerations. This species attains 4 to 5 feet in length. The common spotted moray eel is a rock and reef dweller.

Gymnothorax nigromarginatus - **BLACK-EDGE MORAY EEL** - The black-edge moray eel, a true fish also, has a powerful, muscular, slender body covered by a tough leathery slimy skin. Two or three median fangs and canine teeth fill the mouth. Both the dorsal and anal fins are continuous with the caudal fin. The pectoral and pelvic fins are absent. Dispersed on the body are whitish stellate spots smaller in size than the eye. A dusky shade of color occurs along the sides of the body. The anal fin is either solid black or brown while the dorsal fin is edged with an interrupted dark margin. The black-edge moray eel is a bottom dweller, found in close association with reefs.

SYMPTOMATOLOGY:

The bite of these eels produces a severe lacerating and tearing puncture-like wound in which there can be considerable superficial tissue loss. There is not complete agreement among investigators the world over that any of the moray eels, particularly the varieties found in he Gulf of Mexico, are venomous. The several species of Gulf eels are seasonally ciguatoxic and may be poisonous if eaten. The symptoms and treatment of poisoning due to ciguatoxic fish ingestion are presented elsewhere in this text.

TREATMENT:

Treatment should include both the use of warm compresses or soaking in tap water as hot as the patient can tolerate; then debridement of the numerous wounds produced by the numerous sharp teeth and suturing of those wounds which are definitely clean and devoid of any devitalized tissue. The patient should be given broad spectrum antibiotics and a tetanus toxoid booster. The wounds should be inspected frequently for the early signs of wound complications, foreign body reaction, or infection including anaerobic granulomatous lesions produced by *Mycobacterium marinum* (26, 47, 48, 61, 62, 63).

TURTLES

Chelonia mydas   —   **GREEN TURTLE** (Fig. 163)

Dermochelys coriacea   —   **LEATHERBACK TURTLE, LUTH BACK TURTLE** (Fig. 164)

Eretmochelys imbricata —   **HAWKSBILL TURTLE, TORTOISE SHELL TURTLE** (Fig. 165)

DESCRIPTION:

Chelonia mydas - **GREEN TURTLE** - Usually only one claw is found on the flipper of this turtle and the jaws lack a beak-like appearance. This turtle is usually found in water of less than 25 meters. It is found more commonly in areas sheltered by reefs where it feeds on algae, such as turtle grass. It is also found in bays and lagoons.

Dermochelys coriacea - **LEATHERBACK TURTLE** - This turtle lacks the outer covering of tortoise shell. Its soft leathery skin, from which its gets it name, is raised into longitudinal ridges. It is the largest of turtles reaching a length of 6 feet or more and a weight of more than half a ton. It is found in deep water near the edge of the Continental Shelf.

Eretmochelys imbricata - **HAWKSBILL TURTLE** - The hawksbill turtle attains its name from the hawk-like head. The upper jaw extends to an overhanging beak. The tortoise shell plates or shields overlap one another. There are 2 claws on the front flippers. The average size of the animal is 4 feet long. It feeds on seaweed and is found close to land in the tropical and subtropical lagoons.

GENERAL:

Although each variety of salt water turtles found in the Texas Gulf of Mexico (the green turtle, leatherback turtle, and the tortoise shell turtle) are nonaggressive, they will bite when molested. The bite can be painful and significantly large.

Poisoning from the marine turtle is one of the lesser known types of intoxications produced by marine organisms. The cases that have been reported are sufficiently severe to be impressive. As in the case of fishes, most of these species are commonly eaten with impunity. For some unknown reason, certain species of marine turtles, under certain circumstances, may become extremely poisonous when eaten. Marine turtles should be eaten with caution. If in doubt, check with local native groups and find out if they are safe to eat in that locality. Turtle liver is especially dangerous to eat.

SYMPTOMATOLOGY:

Their bites are strictly traumatic and nonvenomous, although the eating of their flesh can be very toxic, even fatal. Symptoms of poisoning generally develop from a few hours to several days after ingestion of the flesh. The initial symptoms are usually nausea, vomiting, diarrhea, severe upper abdominal pain, and dizziness. Other symptoms reported include dry burning sensation of the lips, tongue, buccal surfaces, and throat. Swallowing becomes very difficult. Excessive salivation is produced. The disturbances of the mouth may take several days to develop, but become progressively severe as time passes. The tongue develops a white coating and the breath becomes very foul. Later the tongue may become covered with multiple pin-head sized reddened papules which may later break down into ulcers. If the victim has been severely poisoned, he tends to become very sleepy and is difficult to wake. If this symptom develops, it is usually a bad sign and death soon follows. Death is believed to be due to liver and kidney damage. About 44% of the victims poisoned by marine turtles die.

TREATMENT:

Treatment of the bites of the marine turtles of the Texas Gulf of Mexico should be handled as any other traumatic wound. There is no specific treatment. Some of the recommendations presented in "Fish Poisoning" (Ciguatoxic Fishes) are pertinent should poisoning occur (26, 47, 48, 61, 62).

SHARKS

Carcharhinus falciformes	— **SILKY SHARK** (Fig. 166)
Carcharhinus leucas	— **BULL SHARK, CUB SHARK, GROUND SHARK, REQUIEM SHARK, SAND SHARK** (Fig. 167)
Carcharhinus limbatus	— **BLACKTIP SHARK, SPOT-FIN SHARK, SPOT-FIN GROUND SHARK** (Fig. 168)
Carcharhinus longimanus	— **OCEANIC WHITETIP SHARK** (Fig. 170)
Ginglymostoma cirratum	— **NURSE SHARK, CAT SHARK, GATA** (Fig. 169)
Negaprion brevirostris	— **LEMON SHARK** (Fig. 171)
Sphyrna lewini	— **SCALLOPED HAMMERHEAD** (Fig. 172)
Squalus acanthias	— **DOGFISH, SPIKED DOGFISH, SPINED DOGFISH** (Fig. 173)

DESCRIPTION:

Carcharinus falciformes - **SILKY SHARK** - The elongate body of this shark has extremely long pectoral fins, small eyes, and long, separate projections extending from the bases of the second dorsal and anal fins. The snout is moderately prolonged and pointed. There is an obvious dermal ridge down the center of the back between the first and second dorsal fins. The silky shark, so named for its sleek-textured skin, attains a 10 foot length, and is colored blue-black or charcoal gray above and grayish-white below. It is commonly found offshore in waters reaching a temperature of 75° F. or higher, although it has been reported to inhabit brackish waters.

Carcharhinus leucas - **BULL SHARK** - This slow-swimming shark is characterized by a moderately short trunk, a very wide head, and a short and broadly rounded snout. The second dorsal fin is much smaller than the first dorsal fin. The presence of both small, yellowish-brown eyes with vertical pupils and small spiracles are characteristic of this aggressive species. Twelve feet is the recorded maximum length of this shark. Its color is gray above and white below. Dark-tipped fins are found only in young sharks.

Carcharhinus limbatus - **BLACKTIP SHARK** - This swift-swimming shark is a smooth-backed specimen with a moderately long pointed snout, elongate body, and long caudal fin. The maximum recorded length of this shark is 9 feet (300 pounds). Its color is either a blue-gray or dusky bronze-gray above and white or yellow below. A band of the dark upper color extends along each side. The pectoral fin tips are dusky or black in the adult, hence the name.

Carcharhinus longimanus - **OCEANIC WHITETIP SHARK** - The elongate body of this shark is characterized by a broadly rounded head and snout. The pectoral fins are elongate, rigid, and blunt. The tip of the first dorsal fin is broadly rounded, while the rear tips of the anal fins extend to a small notch just anterior of the caudal fin. This species attains a length of 13 feet. Its color is either a light gray, pale brown, or slate-blue above and a yellowish-white below. The fins are white-tipped mottled with gray.

This shark is found most often in the open sea and does not enter water below 71° F. It infrequently ventures close to shore.

Ginglymostoma cirratum - **NURSE SHARK** - This is a small thick-skinned shark with a moderately stout trunk and a broadly rounded, noticeably short snout. The broad, asymmetrical caudal fin is about 1/3 the length of the body. The nostrils are connected to the thick-lipped mouth by deep external grooves. Fleshy barbels ("whiskers") are located on the front margin of each nostril. The eyes are small and lack a nictitating membrane. The color of this

201

animal is both a grayish-brown, often marked with yellow, above and a paler shade of the grayish-brown below.

During the day the nurse shark is found inshore in a shallow water area (2 -10 feet in depth) over sandy beach, while it forages in deeper water at night. This sluggish shark is often found lying on the sea floor in schools and is readily approached and may even be stepped on.

Negaprion brevirostris - **LEMON SHARK** - This shark has a moderately stout trunk, a broad neck, wide pectoral fins, two nearly equal-sized dorsal fins, and a short round snout. The maximum length of the lemon shark is 11 feet. Its color is usually yellow-brown above with a white or pale yellow belly.

The lemon shark is strictly an inshore species preferring the clear shallow waters located over sand and often inhabits brackish water. The adults are caught at depths down to 20 fathoms. There is some evidence that they cruise in schools of 20 or more offshore near the surface in warm waters.

Sphyrna lewini - **SCALLOPED HAMMERHEAD** - The hammerhead is characterized by a well-developed nasal groove that extends along the front of the hammer-shaped head. The anterior margin of the hammerhead is scalloped and convex with a deep, rounded indention occurring at the midline. The gray or black-tipped pectoral fins are large and elongated. The color of this animal is light gray above and white below. This hammerhead attains a length of not more than 10 feet.

Squalus acanthias - **DOGFISH SHARK** - This shark is characterized by a small slender body, pointed snout, and rather high, exposed dorsal spines anterior to each dorsal fin. The adult length ranges from 2 to 3 1/2 feet with a weight of 5 to 15 pounds. The dogfish is slate colored above; sometimes tinged with brown and gray-to-white below.

The dogfish ranges widely throughout the open seas of the Continental Shelf, and only rarely is found in water deeper than 100 fathoms. It congregates in large schools and migrates north and inshore in the spring, then returns to the south, moving offshore, in the autumn.

GENERAL:

The preceding descriptions of several of the sharks found in the Gulf of Mexico is but a representative sample of the over 50 species that inhabit this body of water.

The extremely large mouth, multiple rows of sharp teeth, extremely powerful jaw muscles, and the characteristic violent shaking of a mouthful of bone and soft tissues renders the shark wound the most formidable and life-threatening traumatic wound of all marine creatures. A single bite by a large shark can be immediately fatal due to massive blood loss. The fatality rate is about 85% worldwide (Figs. 174, 175).

TREATMENT:

Treatment includes very prompt control of hemorrhage by "pressure point" technique or a properly placed arterial tourniquet proximal to the wound utilizing a strap, a belt, or a tight roll of clothing. The victim must be removed to the shore where a plasma-expander must be administered intravenously if it is available. The patient must be promptly rushed to an emergency medical facility where whole blood transfusions and definitive surgical treatment can be provided upon arrival. Fortunately, shark attacks on humans are exceedingly rare along the Texas Gulf coast and the Texas Continental Shelf.

Several species of shark found in the Gulf have been implicated in poisoning produced after ingestion of their flesh or liver. Symptoms and treatment of fish poisoning are described in another section of this text (3, 26, 47, 48).

Sphyraena barracuda — GREAT BARRACUDA (Fig. 176 a, b)

DESCRIPTION:

The compressed pike-like body of this swift-moving predator reaches a length of 6 - 8 feet. The large mouth of the barracuda is filled with fang-like unequal canine teeth. The jutting lower jaw has a fleshy tip.

The large-scaled body is silvery in color. The great barracuda is abundant about reefs where it forages. However, it is seen both offshore and inshore. The adults may inhabit deeper water ranging from 120 to 240 feet; however, most barracuda are caught in surface waters.

The habits of this fish include a northward migraton, at a rate of 2 miles a day, in the spring and summer and a southward migration in the fall and winter. Solitary barracuda over 3 feet long are more prone to attack humans.

SYMPTOMATOLOGY:

The great barracuda has strong jaws and a single row of long, sharp teeth. Unlike the shark, the great barracuda has a long pointed set of jaws and does not shake the victim when it bites. Indeed and in fact a barracuda of four feet of length or larger is capable of producing a sizeable, pyramidal, clean, traumatic wound in which major nerves and vessels can be severed. Fortunately, in the Texas Gulf of Mexico either unprovoked or provoked attacks on human beings by the great barracuda are exceedingly rare. Under certain environmental conditions, when spawning or mating, the flesh of the great barracuda is poisonous. Symptoms and treatment of poisoning is delineated under "Fish Poisoning" (Ciguatoxic Fishes).

TREATMENT:

Efficient and prompt first aid of the victim by the use of "pressure point" or a tourniquet proximal to the wound to control arterial bleeding is of paramount importance as a life saving measure. Also, the victim should then be transported to an emergency care facility as quickly as possible. At the emergency facility plasma expanders and/or whole blood should be administered as indicated. Definitive surgical debridement and repair of the wound or wounds should be performed (16, 20, 26, 27, 41, 47, 61, 62).

Astroscopus y-graecum   —   **SOUTHERN STARGAZER, ELECTRIC STARGAZER** (Fig. 177)

DESCRIPTION:

The southern stargazer gets its name from its upward directed eyes located on the top of its head. In front of the small prominent eyes are 2 or 3 small blunt spines. The dorsal fin also has 3 - 5 spines. This fish attains an average length of 15 inches. It is dark brown in color above and paler below. The upper parts are densely covered with small, rounded, white spots (each surrounded by a black ring). The caudal and dorsal fins have black and white stripes. The pectoral fins are brown or black with a white edge on the margin of the fin. This fish is often found burrowed in the sand in the shallow waters of sandy bays with only the eyes and mouth exposed.

GENERAL:

The species of stargazers in the Texas Gulf of Mexico contain a venom apparatus consisting of two shoulder spines, one on either side, each of which protrudes through a sheath of skin. Venom glands are attached to the spines. Each spine has a double groove through which the venom flows.

SYMPTOMATOLOGY:

There is no reliable information available regarding the clinical characteristics of wounds produced by stargazers; however, the literature does contain reports of fatalities. Stargazers should be handled with extreme care in order to avoid being jabbed by the shoulder spines. At least one species can produce an electric shock from "electric muscle organs" located in the head region just behind the eyes.

TREATMENT:

Efforts in treating such a venomous fish "sting" should be directed toward achieving three objectives: (1) alleviating pain, (2) combatting the effects of the venom, (3) preventing secondary infection. The pain results from the effects of the trauma produced by the fish spine, venom, and the introduction of slime and other irritating foreign substances into the wound. Wounds of this type should be properly irrigated (wash with either cold salt water or sterile saline if available). It may be necessary to make a small incision across the wound and then apply immediate suction and irrigation. At any rate, the wound should be sucked promptly in order to remove as much of the venom as possible. Most authorities recommend soaking the injured part of the body in hot water for 30 minutes to 1 hour inorder to neutralize the protein venom. Following the soaking procedure, debridement and further cleansing of the wound should be carried out. Broad spectrum antibiotics should be given, as well as injectable antihistamines, and a tetanus toxoid booster. A bulky pressure dressing should be applied to the wound area. The wound should be inspected frequently for any evidence of the development of wound complications, foreign body reaction, or infection including anaerobic granulomatous lesions produced by *Mycobacterium marinum.* The electric shock produced by one species is merely a nuisance and not dangerous to life (28, 30, 47, 48, 55, 56, 63).

Bagre marinus — **GAFF-TOP SAIL CATFISH** (Fig. 178)

DESCRIPTION:
The chin of the gaff-top sail catfish is equipped with four barbels ("whiskers"), one short pair on the lower chin and a long pair extending from the upper jaw. The silver-blue skin of this catfish is thick, very slimy and lacks scales. The caudal fin is deeply forked. The most distinguishing feature of this fish is the extended rays of the dorsal and pectoral fins. Moreover, spines are located immediately ahead of each of these fins. This fish attains a maximum length of two feet. It is often found in the surf in the intertidal zone.

SYMPTOMATOLOGY:
The stab wounds resulting from the careless handling of this variety of catfish are extremely painful and although there has been no proven venom, the local tissue reaction is similar to one of envenomation. The wounds are extremely painful and attended by cyanosis, ischemia, and then rapid, massive swelling. Most of this local response is due to the introduction of the slime from the spine into the wound.

TREATMENT:
The injured parts should be immersed in hot tap water for 30 minutes to 1 hour. Then the wounds should be probed and debrided, but not sutured. A bulky pressure dressing should be placed over the wounds and the wounds inspected frequently for any evidence of early signs of wound complications, foreign body reaction, or infection including anaerobic granulomatous lesions produced by *Mycobacterium marinum.* The patient should be given

a tetanus toxoid booster and placed on broad spectrum antibiotics. Any signs and symptoms of systemic intoxication must be promptly treated symptomatically. Supportive care should be rendered (29, 30, 47, 48, 55, 56, 63).

Arius felis   —   **SEA CATFISH, COMMON SEA CATFISH, HARD HEAD**
(Galeichthys felis)   **SEA CATFISH** (Fig. 179)

DESCRIPTION:
     The elongate, torpedo-shaped body of the sea catfish terminates posteriorly in a deeply forked caudal fin. The most distinguishing features are the six long barbels ("whiskers") on its head, the fleshy adipose fin located behind the dorsal fin, and the scaleless slimy skin. The rays of the dorsal and pectoral fins are not greatly elongated. This is a very abundant, nocturnal, inshore coastal species which occasionally enters brackish water. Its color is dark silvery gray above and white beneath. It reaches a length of about one foot.

SYMPTOMATOLOGY:
     The larger varieties can produce an extremely painful and injurious wound by piercing the soft tissues of man with its dorsal and pectoral fin barbs which may be followed with systemic symptoms similar to that of envenomation. Some investigators feel that at least one variety of marine catfish injuries are venomous, although this has not been proven experimentally or clinically. Halstead and co-workers identified a venom apparatus in the sea catfish in 1953, but could not find proof of human envenomation.

TREATMENT:
     These wounds should be treated with wet heat, elevation, irrigation, and debridement of the puncture wound, compression dressings, and inspection of the wound at frequent intervals for any detection of early signs or symptoms of wound complications, foreign body reaction, or infection including anaerobic granulomatous lesions produced by *Mycobacterium marinum*. The patient should be given both broad spectrum antibiotics and a tetanus toxoid booster. Clinical symptoms and signs of systemic intoxication must be treated symptomatically. Supportive care should be provided (29, 30, 47, 48, 55, 56, 63).

206

Lepisosteus spatula — **ALLIGATOR GAR** (Fig. 180)

DESCRIPTION:
This fish has heavy external armor which consists of rhombic, flat plates. These enameled scales are in an oblique series from the ventral fins to the middle of the back. The snout is usually shorter than the rest of the head. The alligator gar can reach 8 - 12 feet in length and may weight several hundred pounds. The dark greenish color of the back blends into a much paler green on the belly of the fish. It is usually found in either shallow weedy areas of estuaries or in bays and shallow ditches. This gar usually appears sluggish, remaining almost motionless in the water for some time, although it can move quite rapidly when chasing food.

SYMPTOMATOLOGY:
This large fish which lives in fresh water, brackish water, or sea water is not aggressive but will bite when intruded upon or teased. Its mouth contains multiple sharp teeth that can inflict a most serious wound. In addition, is outer surface is covered by many parasites, including barnacles. If the animal rubs against the skin it can produce very painful, deep, abrasive wounds which may be very slow to heal.

The flesh of this gar contains the toxin tetrodotoxin and may produce serious poisoning if eaten. The symptoms and treatment are discussed under "Fish Poisoning" (Tetrodotoxic Fish) in another section of this text.

TREATMENT:
The control of hemorrhage by "pressure point" or a tourniquet placed proximal to the wound is essential in treating a bite by this fish. A serious bite by a gar must be treated by surgical debridement as any other jagged and penetrating traumatic wound with tissue loss. The abraded wound should be rinsed thoroughly, and all foreign particles removed, and then dressed with antibiotic pressure dressings. The wound should be inspected frequently for any evidence of early signs of wound complication, foreign body reaction, or infection including anaerobic granulomatous lesions produced by *Mycobacterium marinum*. The patient should be given a tetanus toxoid booster and placed on broad spectrum antibiotics (16, 26, 47, 61, 62, 63).

Diodon hystrix — **PORCUPINE FISH** (Fig. 181 a, b)

DESCRIPTION:
The porcupine fish has a beak-like jaw with fused undivided teeth in the upper and lower jaws. When disturbed, the porcupine fish inflates its small,

black-spotted, strongly spined body with water and in this spherical state measures up to 3 feet in diameter. When not inflated in seldom exceeds a length of more than 22 inches. The color is pale, ventrally, with a yellow ground color. The largest spots are found in front of the dorsal fin. Smaller spots are found on a naked area around the mouth. It is common everywhere in tropical seas.

SYMPTOMATOLOGY:

The porcupine fish produces traumatic injury of either a minor or rather serious degree due to its ability to inflate and extend its extremely numerous and sharp spines. If a hand, or any portion of the human body, comes in contact with this fish, one can sustain numerous, deep, penetrating, painful, non-venomous wounds. Ingestion of the flesh of this fish can produce poisoning. The symptoms and treatment of this poisoning are delineated under ".Fish Poisoning" (Tetrodotoxic fishes) in another section of this text.

TREATMENT:

Treatment of the puncture wounds of the porcupine fish should be handled as any traumatic puncture wound that is dealt with commonly within either a first aid establishment or an emergency room with the understanding that these wounds are highly infective and contaminated and should be irrigated with copious quantities of an antibiotic or saline solution. The patient should receive a tetanus toxoid booster, broad spectrum antibiotics, and frequent observation of the wound for any signs of wound complication, foreign body reaction, or infection including anaerobic granulomatous lesions produced by *Mycobacterium marinum* (26, 47, 48, 62, 63).

Holocentrus ascensionis — **SQUIRREL FISH** (Fig. 182)

DESCRIPTION:

The squirrel fish is recognized by its compressed body, oblique small mouth, strong spine located anterior to the posterior margin of the gill flap, and very long dagger-like anal spine. This fish is bright red in color with shiny longitudinal streaks along the rows of scales. The fins are light red, while the head is quite red with an oblique white bar descending backwards from the eye. It may attain a length of 2 feet, and is found around rocks in reef areas.

SYMPTOMATOLOGY:

Handling of this fish can result in both painful bites and non-venomous puncture wounds from his numerous spines. Ingestion of the flesh of the squirrel fish may produce symptoms of poisoning. Treatment of this poisoning is delineated under "Fish Poisoning" (Ciguatoxic Fishes).

TREATMENT:
    In treating these traumatic wounds, hot soaks for 30 minutes to 1 hour, cleansing and irrigation of the wounds with an antibiotic solution, and the application of a compression dressing are recommended. Administer a tetanus toxoid booster; start a broad spectrum antibiotic; and observe the wounds frequently for any early signs of wound complication, foreign body reaction, or infection including anaerobic granulomatous lesions produced by *Mycobacterium marinum* (26, 47, 48, 62, 63).

Opsanus beta —   COMMON TOADFISH, OYSTER FISH, SLIMER, OYSTER DOGFISH, GULF TOADFISH (Fig. 183)

DESCRIPTION:
    The broad, flat, toad-like head of the toadfish features a large mouth with strong powerful jaws. There is a broad flap of tissue above each eye. Short flaps of tissue are seen on both the lower and upper jaw. The lower portion of the gill flap ends in a long sharp spine. Anterior to the dorsal fin, is a series of 3 short sharp spines which are elevated when the fish is disturbed. The paired pectoral fins are thick and fleshy and are colored with light or dark bands. This fish is colored a dusky olive with black markings forming irregular indistinct bars. The belly and sides of the head are lighter in color. It is strictly a bottom-dwelling fish, burrowing beneath rocks in shallow or deep water. It may attain a length of 15 inches.

SYMPTOMATOLOGY:
    All species of toadfish have both dorsal and opercular spines and some can inject a venom into a handler. However, very little is known about the venom and its effects.

TREATMENT:
    Immerse the injured part in hot tap water for 1 hour, and administer parenterally an antihistamine and a tetanus toxoid booster. Start the patient on broad spectrum antibiotics. Cover the wound with a bulky pressure dressing, inspecting it frequently for any signs or symptoms of wound complication, foreign body reaction, or infection including anaerobic granulomatous lesions produced by *Mycobacterium marinum*. Signs and symptoms of systemic intoxication are treated symptomatically. Supportive treatment should be provided (25, 26, 30, 48, 56, 63).

STINGRAYS

Aetobatus narinari   —   **SPOTTED STINGRAY, SPOTTED EAGLE RAY** (Fig. 184)

Dasyatis americana   —   **SOUTHERN STINGRAY** (Fig. 185)

Dasyatis sabina   —   **STINGAREE, ATLANTIC STINGRAY** (Fig. 186)

Narcine brasiliensis   —   **LESSER ELECTRIC RAY, CRAMPFISH** (Fig. 187)

Urolophus jamaicensis —   **YELLOW SPOTTED STINGRAY** (Fig. 188)

DESCRIPTION:

Aetobatus narinari - **SPOTTED STINGRAY** - The depressed disc of this ray has slightly convex anterior borders and concave posterior borders. It is twice as broad as long. A small dorsal fin is present. The slender finless tail is much longer than the disc and is armed with a venomous spine ("sting"). The large "sting" is located at the base of the tail. The pointed pectoral fins, used in swimming and leaping out of the water, are either opposite the eyes or entirely interrupted at that point, making the head and single-lobed snout conspicuously marked off from the rest of the body. Some specimens reach an 11 foot wing width and a weight of 450 pounds. The primary color of this ray is brown with small round white dots. Its habitat includes both shallow bays and estuaries. It is an inshore species, which is distributed world-wide in tropical seas.

Dasyatis americana - **SOUTHERN STINGRAY** - This ray has a depressed quadrangular disc slightly wider than long. Three series of shoulder spines and a small, round, light-colored spot located in the middle of the forehead are two features of this animal. The tail, with a simple keel above and a wing-like expansion below, terminates in a long, whip-like appendage to which is attached a venomous spine located close to the base of the tail. This ray is a common inhabitant of both brackish and fresh water, swimming at moderate depths but more commonly resting partially exposed on the bottom in shallow water, sheltered bays, shoal lagoons, river mouths, and shady areas between patch reefs.

Dasyatis sabina - **STINGAREE** - This ray has a subcircular depressed disc and snout with the anterior margins of the pectorals appearing concave near the snout. The tail is less than twice as long as the disc and tapers to a fine point. A venomous barb is located about half-way down the tail. Long, wing-like expansions occur below the tail, which is rough with small prickles similar to those scattered over the head. A series of spines is located on the back. The ray is primarily yellowish-brown in color. It inhabits both estuaries and fresh-water streams, burrowing into the mud with the eyes and a portion of the tail exposed.

Narcine brasiliensis - **LESSER ELECTRIC RAY** - The highly flattened, smooth, unarmored disc of this ray is oval. The short shark-like tail terminates in a small caudal fin. The snout is broadly rounded, and is supported by branched cartilage which can be felt. The spiracles are located posterior to the eyes and have roughened edges. Coloration varies from nearly uniformly brown or yellow in deep water, to either being marked with dark spots and dashes or with a dark band. The lesser electric ray rarely attains a length of 2 feet, but can generate 40 volts with specialized muscles appearing as kidney-shaped structures located between the head and the pectoral fins. It burrows in the sand in the tidal zone.

Urolophus jamaicensis - **YELLOW SPOTTED STINGRAY** - The yellow spotted ray is characterized by an oval depressed disc which is slightly longer than broad. The snout does not project. The skin is sparsely covered with small prickles. The caudal appendage (tail), to which the stinging spine is attached, is short and muscular with a well-developed caudal fin. The color of the ray is brown, sprinkled with small yellow spots and edged with darker yellow. It is generally common along the coast.

GENERAL:

Stingrays are rather numerous in the sand and muddy bottoms of the shallow water, where wading, floating, and swimming are popular along the beachfronts of the Texas Gulf of Mexico.

Prevention from envenomation by the stingray in shallow water can be accomplished by using a "shuffle walk": with each step, place the heel of the foot in the sand and swish the foot rapidly from side-to-side. This action will frighten away any stingray in the path. Injury is sustained when the fish is accidentally stepped on. Upon this contact the ray lashes out with its tail from which a venomous barb extrudes. The barb pierces the skin and soft tissue, producing either a jagged laceration, a typical puncture wound, or a stellate wound (Fig. 189). Portions of the "saw-tooth" stinger frequently are left in the wound, attended by the leaking of venom from the stinger into the wound.

SYMPTOMATOLOGY:

The pain due to the envenomation is excruciating. It radiates proximally, thus distinguishing this injury from one produced by a jagged inanimate object. Muscle weakness, progressing to paralysis, may occur. In a small percentage of victims the intense pain persists for several hours accompanied by a fall in blood pressure, rapid pulse, chills, nausea, vomiting, and collapse.

211

TREATMENT:
   Remove the victim from the water and promptly submerge the wounded part (usually the foot or ankle) in tap water as hot as can be tolerated for from 30 minutes to 1 hour. The venom is a protein and heat labile. The soaking in hot water accomplishes two important things: 1) deactivation of the venom and 2) decrease in pain. Remove the part from the hot tap water, and, under good illumination, irrigate the wound with an antibacterial or antibiotic solution. Tease out any remnants of the exoskeleton and any other foreign material found in the wound. Then replace the part in tap water as hot as tolerated for 1 hour. DO NOT suture the wound. Apply a bulky pressure dressing, administer an antihistamine parenterally and a tetanus toxoid booster; and start the patient on a broad-spectrum antibiotic. For relief of pain on admission, morphine or meperidine may be indicated. The dressing should be changed frequently and the wound inspected for any signs of wound complication, foreign body reaction, or infection including anaerobic granulomatous lesions produced by *Mycobacterium marinum*. Clinical signs and symptoms of systemic intoxication are treated symptomatically and any indicated supportive care should be rendered (12, 25, 26, 30, 45, 47, 48, 50, 53, 55, 56, 63).

COELENTERATES

Acropora palmata	—	**ELK HORN CORAL** (Fig. 191)
Aurelia aurita	—	**MOON JELLY** (Fig. 190)
Chiropsalmus quadrigatus	—	**SEA WASP** (Figs. 192, 193)
Cyanea capillata	—	**HAIRY STINGER, LION'S MANE** (Figs. 194, 195)
Millipora complanata	—	**FIRE CORAL** (Fig. 196, a, b, c,)
Physalia physalis	—	**PORTUGUESE MAN-O-WAR** (Figs. 197, 198, 199)

DESCRIPTION:
   Acropora palmata - **ELK HORN CORAL** - Elk horn coral is a brownish-yellow coral in which flattened frond-like branches are present. The coral thus takes the appearance of the horns of an elk. The colonies are branches with each branch composed of an individual polyp forming an axis with several radial polyps budding off from it. The coral is found in the Florida Keys, Bahamas, West Indies, Gulf of Mexico Flower Gardens, and other warm water reefs where it is not exposed to heavy surf.

212

Aurelia aurita - **MOON JELLY** - The pulsating saucer-shaped bell of the moon jellyfish measures 10 to 12 inches across and numerous short tentacles extend from it. The top of the flattened bell reveals a four-leaf clover design, formed by the reproductive organs (yellow in the female and lavender in the male). The moon jelly is a shallow water inhabitant; and although it is carried by the winds and currents, it is capable of locomoting on its own.

Chiropsalmus quadrigatus - **SEA WASP** - This free-swimming jellyfish assumes a square-bell shape in the water. Claw-like tentacles attached to each of the four corners of the bell are highly contractile. The outer tentacular surface contains rings of stinging nematocysts. Although this creature is carried by tides, currents, and winds; it is a rhythmic, strong swimmer. Its swimming is achieved by active pulsations of the bell. This coelenterate is a danger to bathers in shallow waters.

Cyanea capillata - **HAIRY STINGER** - The hairy stinger is a free-swimming jellyfish moving by pulsations of the saucer-shaped, 3 to 7 feet in diameter, bell. It is a shapeless firm mass of either yellow-pink or pale orange jelly with short yellow-red tentacles extending from the outer bell perimeter. Longer orange-pink tentacles, which may extend down to 75 feet, are attached to the bell, being located inside the shorter tentacles. The hairy stinger is found drifting inshore at depths of 2 - 10 feet.

Millipora complanta - **FIRE CORAL** - Fire coral is a stationary coelenterate form. It is strongly branched and is found either in solid lumps or forming a large, massive surface of lime carbonate. The polyp itself conforms to dead corals, sea fans, *et cetera,* in which it forms an encrusting exoskeleton not having any identifying features of its own. Characteristic shapes are upright, clavate, blade-like, or branching calcareous growths on crustaceans or on other corals. It frequently imparts a light, velvet-like appearance to the coral, *et cetera* on which it grows.

Physalia physalis - **PORTUGUESE MAN-O-WAR** - The man-o-war, a colonial hydroid, depends mainly on the wind, current, and tides for its locomotion. The large balloon-like float may reach a length of 4 to 12 inches. Extending down from the float are numerous long tentacles, some reaching to lengths of 100 feet, which are used in feeding, fishing, and sexual reproduction. These tentacles contain numerous (700 - 900 per inch of tentacle) stinging cells (nematocysts). It is these stinging cells that are the source of numerous human injuries each year along the Texas Gulf coast. These tentacles rhythmically contract and relax. The man-o-war is found either floating on top of the water or washed up on beaches. In those that are beached, the venom in the stinging cells remain "potent" for many days.

GENERAL:

In the Texas Gulf of Mexico, a swimmer or diver can sustain a sting of either minor or major significance from any one of the several coelenterates that inhabit these waters. During the summer months these creatures can be found in considerable numbers along the beaches of Texas.

SYMPTOMATOLOGY:

An intense stinging and burning .sensation of the involved areas of skin, attended by a marked erythema, are the common symptoms and signs. However, extensive stings, either by the tentacles of a large Portuguese man-o-war or by the sea wasp, can result in throbbing or shooting pains, unconsciousness, muscular cramps, abdominal rigidity, nausea, vomiting, severe backache, inability to speak, frothing at the mouth, sensation of constriction of the throat, respiratory difficulty, paralysis, delirium, convulsions, and death. In many of the non-fatal cases, permanent pigmented scarring of the involved areas occurs.

TREATMENT:

Treatment must be directed toward accomplishing two objectives (relieving pain and alleviating effects of the toxin). To relieve pain first remove adherent portions of tentacles promptly with protection to the hands such as gloves, a hat, a shirt, a towel, *et cetera.* Then splash a generous volume of rubbing alcohol over the involved skin areas followed with a generous sprinkling of Adolph's Unseasoned Meat Tenderizer over the involved areas. If the skin areas involved are extensive and intensely painful, the injection of a narcotic analgesic is indicated.

The rubbing alcohol "fixes" all remaining alive nematocysts, thus preventing further stinging. The meat tenderizer neutralizes the protein toxin by the action of the proteolytic enzyme papain on the toxin. Intravenous injection of calcium gluconate is recommended for the control of muscular spasms. Parenteral administration of an antihistamine should be undertaken promptly. In critical cases, artificial respiration, cardiac and respiratory stimulants, and other forms of supportive measures may be required. There are no known antidotes.

The sea wasp found in Australian waters is probably the most venomous marine organism known. It may produce death within 3 to 8 minutes. The species found in the Gulf of Mexico, however, is considered only as venomous as a large Portuguese man-o-war (4, 5, 6, 7, 9, 10, 11, 13, 21, 23, 26, 31, 33, 34, 37, 38, 40, 43, 47, 48, 51, 54, 55, 56, 59, 60, 64).

BRISTLEWORMS

Chloeia viridis   —   **SEA MOUSE, BRISTLE WORM** (Fig. 200)

Eurythroe complanta   —   **FIRE WORM, BRISTLE WORM** (Fig. 201)

Hermodice carunculata   —   **BRISTLE WORM, FIRE WORM** (Fig. 202)

DESCRIPTION:
> *Chloeia viridis* - **SEA MOUSE** - This soft-bodied invertebrate is a polychaete worm with a cylindrical, elongate, segmented body. Each of the segments bears a pair of elongate bristle-like locomotory appendages. This species is common about reefs and is encountered upon turning over rocks or pieces of coral.

> *Eurythroe complanata* - **BRISTLE WORM** - This red-pink annelid worm is characterized by a segmented, elongate body with each segment bearing paired retractable setae or bristle-like structures. The free-moving bristle worm is encountered upon turning over rocks or coral boulders on a reef and may be iridescent.

> *Hermodice carunculata* - **FIRE WORM** - The fire worm is a segmented annelid worm with an elongate body. Each segment bears a pair of setae or soft white glass-like bristles containing a venom. The head region bears tentacles also. The body of this worm is usually 8 inches long and is rose-pink in color. It is most frequently found under rocks and boulders in reef areas.

SYMPTOMATOLOGY:
> All of the bristle worms inject their bristles or setae into any skin with which they come into contact. These appendages are venomous and produce local pain and swelling usually of a minor degree.

TREATMENT:
> Since there is no known specific antidote for the envenomation from the setae (bristles) of these worms, and a standard treatment is used for all of the bristle worms. This consists of soaking the part in hot water for thirty minutes followed with the application of ammonia water or rubbing alcohol. After the skin is dried in the air, scotch tape is used to remove the bristles (23, 24, 26, 47, 48, 62).

Stichopus bandiotus — **SEA CUCUMBER** (Fig. 203)

DESCRIPTION:

The sausage or cucumber-like body of this invertebrate, which may reach 12 or more inches, lacks spines and arms. The skin is leathery, having a few small, scattered warty glands capable of secreting a repellent. Tentacles circle around the mouth. Glands secreting repelling fluids used in defense are found at the posterior end of the body. When disturbed, the sea cucumber produces a glandular secretion, followed with evisceration, that is, the gut organs exit through the mouth, and in time new viscera regenerate. The sea cucumber is a successful burrower due to the very muscular flexible body wall. It is found in lagoons, bays, and offshore reefs.

GENERAL:

The sea cucumber is a member of the Echinoderm group, just as the sea urchin. This variety of sea cucumber of the Texas Gulf of Mexico is only nominally venomous, but contact with them is painful. No spines are present.

SYMPTOMATOLOGY:

When these creatures are handled, they produce a painful stinging sensation, followed by mild-swelling, itching, and redness. Ingestion of its flesh has been reported to be mildly toxic.

TREATMENT:

This sea cucumber should never be handled unless one is wearing heavy gloves. Soaking of the injured part in hot tap water for 30 minutes followed by the generous application of rubbing alcohol or ammonia water should suffice (23, 24, 26).

CONE SHELLS

Conus floridanus — **FLORIDA CONE** (Fig. 205)

Conus ranunculus — **ATLANTIC AGATE CONE** (Fig. 206)

Conus sozoni — **SOZON'S CONE** (Fig. 207)

Conus spurius — **ALPHABET CONE** (Fig. 204)

DESCRIPTION:

Conus floridanus - **FLORIDA CONE** - This shallow-water inhabitant has the exact outline of a cone, is moderately high-spired, and has a 12-whoreled shell. The flattened shoulder of the wide end of this gastropod is marked off by an acute keel. The opening for the soft-bodied animal is long and narrow with a simple lip. A creamy-white ground color is accented with yellow bands and/or dotted rows. The shell on this invertebrate mollusc attains a length of 2 inches.

Conus ranunculus - **ATLANTIC AGATE CONE** - A gray-white ground color is often splotched irregularly with chocolate brown on this cone. The body whorls are moderately convex and rounded over the shoulder at the wide end of the cone shell. Numerous fine wavy spiral threads are found on each whorl. It is reported to attain 2 3/4 inches in length.

Conus sozoni - **SOZON'S CONE** - This is a rare cone shell of the Gulf of Mexico. A yellow-brown ground color is marked with bandings and the spire is gently sloped. The shell is encircled with brown spots. It can attain 2 inches in length.

Conus spurius - **ALPHABET CONE** - The shell is creamy-white, approximately 2 1/2 inches long from spire to tapered end, and exhibits a variety of patterns consisting of spiral rows of interrupted, squarish, orange-yellow spots. At the center, the elevated spire gives a convex contour to the top. The sides of the shell are typically smooth, and the base has cut-in lines. The foot and siphon on this cone are usually brightly colored. It is nocturnal in habit and is commonly found on sand in 1 to 50 feet of water.

GENERAL:

The small number of varieties of cone shells that are found in the Texas Gulf of Mexico produce their injury in a similar manner. The venom apparatus of cone shells consists of the venom bulb, venom duct, radular sheath, and radular teeth. The pharynx and proboscis, which are part of the digestive system, also play an important role as accessory organs. The venom apparatus lies in a cavity within the animal. It is believed that preparatory to stinging, the radular teeth, which are housed in the radular sheath, are released into the pharynx and thence to the proboscis, where they are grasped for thrusting into the flesh of the victim. The venom, which is believed to be produced by the venom duct, is probably forced under pressure by contraction of the venom bulb and duct into the radular sheath, thereby being forced into the coiled radular teeth.

SYMPTOMATOLOGY:

The stings produced by *Conus* are of the puncture wound variety. Localized ischemia, cyanosis, numbness in the area about the wound, or a sharp stinging or burning sensation are usually the initial symptoms. Numbness and tingling begin at the wound site and may spread rapidly, involving the entire body (particularly pronounced about the lips and mouth). In severe cases paralysis may be present. Respiratory distress is usually absent. Coma may ensue. Death is said to be the result of cardiac failure.

TREATMENT:

Prevention is the most important modality of treatment which amounts to being careful to avoid coming into contact with the soft parts of this beast. If one must grasp the animal for a specimen, he should have gloves on and use the large or bulbous, non-tapering end of the creature along its posterior aspect so as to avoid the proboscis which can be thrust outward from the tapered part of the shell. There is no known specific treatment. The cases of cone shell stings must be managed like all other venomous fish stings including moist heat, irrigation of the wound with antibiotic solution, and loose bulky bandaging of the wound. A parenteral antihistamine and a tetanus toxoid booster should be administered. Signs and symptoms of systemic intoxication are treated symptomatically. Supportive care should be provided (14, 15, 17, 26, 35, 47, 48, 51, 55, 56, 59, 60).

Scorpaena plumieri — **WEST INDIAN SCORPION FISH,
SPOTTED SCORPION FISH** (Fig. 208 a, b)

DESCRIPTION:

The body of the scorpion fish is short and thick, with firm, large, body scales having membranaceous flaps. The scaleless head contains numerous grooves, pits, and many fleshy flaps. The dorsal, anal, and pelvic spines are venomous. The white-spotted dorsal fin is thick and fleshy. It is basically sandy in color with two broad, black shades on the body and head with dark lines radiating from the eye. The belly is purple. The caudal fin is variously mottled with three pale and three black bands, the white anal fin is variegated with red and black. The broad pectoral fins feature white spots on a black background. The spotted scorpion fish reaches a length of 1 foot, is a reef dweller, and is often seen lying motionless on the bottom.

GENERAL:

Members of the genus *Scorpaena* are for the most part shallow water bottom dwellers found in bays, along sandy beaches, rocky coast lines, or coral reefs (from the intertidal zone to depths of 50 fathoms or more). Their habit of concealing themselves in crevices, among debris, under rocks, or in seaweed, together with their protective coloration which blends them almost perfectly into their surrounding environment makes them difficult to see.

218

When they are removed from the water, they have the defensive habit of erecting their spiny dorsal fin and flurrying out their armed gill covers, pectoral, pelvic, and anal fins. The pectoral fins, although dangerous in appearance, are unarmed. The venom organs of these fish differ from the other scorpion fish of the world in that the Gulf varieties have short heavy spines and harbor an elongated venom gland; all of which is covered by a thick layer of warty skin. This fish is particularly dangerous because of its camouflage appearance, and frequently resembles a large clump of mud or debris.

SYMPTOMATOLOGY:

The symptoms produced by the various species of scorpion fishes are essentially the same, varying in degree rather than in quality. The pain is usually described as immediate, intense, sharp, shooting, or throbbing; radiating from the affected part. The area about the wound becomes ischemic and then cyanotic. The pain produced by most scorpion fishes generally continues for only a few hours. The area in the immediate vicinity of the wound gradually becomes cyanotic, surrounded by a zone of redness, swelling, and heat. Subsequent sloughing of the tissues about the wound site may occur. The wound becomes numb. The skin for some distance from the site of injury becomes painful to touch. Sometimes, complete paralysis of the limb may ensue. Swelling of the entire affected member takes place, frequently to such an extent that movement of the part is impaired. Other symptoms which may be present are cardiac failure, delerium, convulsion, various nervous disturbances, nausea, vomiting, lymphangiitis, swelling of the lymph nodes, joint aches, fever, respiratory distress, and death. Complete recovery from a severe scorpion fish sting may require many months and have an adverse effect on the general health of the victim.

TREATMENT:

Treatment is exactly the same as for other venomous fish stings, that is, soaking in hot tap water for 30 minutes to 1 hour, debridement of the wound, and the administration of a parenteral antihistamine, a broad spectrum antibiotic, and a tetanus toxoid booster. Change the dressing of the wound frequently to observe for any development of gas gangrene. Clinical signs and symptoms of systemic intoxication are treated symptomatically. Appropriate supportive care should be rendered. A specific antidote is as yet unavailable (25, 26, 30, 47, 48, 55, 56, 57).

Fish
Poisoning

CIGUATOXIC FISHES

Ciguatera is a type of poisoning produced by a large variety of tropical marine reef or shore fishes. More than 300 different species have been incriminated to date. Apparently any marine fish under the proper circumstances may become involved with this type of poison, since all of the species listed as poisonous are commonly eaten in some localities and are considered good fishes. It is therefore believed that these fishes become poisonous because of their food habits. Ciguatera is a serious problem in certain tropical areas. It is unfortunately unpredictable and therefore exceedingly difficult to control. The edibility of fishes in an island area have been known to change suddenly. For example, ciguatera intoxications first began to appear in the islands of Midway, Johnson, Palmyra, Fanning, and Christmas about the 1943 and were caused by eating fishes which had previously been known to be edible.

SYMPTOMATOLOGY:

Tingling about the lips, tongue, and throat followed by numbness may develop either immediately, or any time within a period of 30 hours after ingestion of the fish. The tingling sensation may be accompanied by such other symptoms as nausea, vomiting, metallic taste, dryness of the mouth, abdominal cramps and diarrhea. The muscles of the mouth, cheeks and jaws may become drawn and spastic with a feeling of numbness. Headache, joint pain, nervousness, prostration, dizziness, pallor, cyanosis, inability to sleep, extreme weakness, and exhaustion are frequently present. The feeling of weakness may become progressively worse until the patient is unable to walk. Muscle pains are generally described as either dull, heavy aches, or cramping sensations; but also may be sharp and shooting, effecting the arms and legs. Victims complain of their teeth feeling loose and painful in their sockets.

Visual disturbances consisting of blurring of vision, temporary blindness, sensitivity to light, and spots before the eyes are not uncommon. Skin disorders are frequently reported consisting of intense itching, red papular rash, blisters, extensive areas of skin loss, especially of the hands and feet, and occasionally ulceration. There may also be loss of hair and nails.

In severe intoxication the nervous symptoms are particularly pronounced. The victim may interpret the feeling as a tingling, burning, "dry ice", or electric shock sensation. Hot objects may give a feeling of cold. Difficulty in walking and a generalized muscular incoordination may become progressively worse. Muscular paralysis, convulsions, and death may ensue. The mortality rate in this type of fish poisoning is relatively low. About 7% of the persons poisoned die. In those instances in which the victim survives, recovery is extremely slow if the person has been severely poisoned. Complete recovery may require many months or even years.

TREATMENT:

With the exception of the Scombroid poisoning in which the patient should be administered an antihistaminic drug, there is no specific treatment. However a few general procedures have been of value in many instances.

The stomach should be emptied at the earliest possible moment. Syrup of ipecac will be effective. If these ingredients are not available, stick a finger down the back of the throat. A cathartic should be administered. In many instances 10% calcium gluconate given intravenously has given prompt relief from the nervous symptoms, whereas in others it has not. Paraldehyde and ether inhalations have been reported to be effective in controlling the convulsions. In patients where excessive production of mucus is present, aspiration and constant turning are essential. Atropine has been found to make the mucus more viscous and difficult to aspirate, therefore it is not recommended. If laryngeal spasm is present, intubation and tracheostomy may be necessary. Oxygen inhalation and intravenous administration of blood, along with parenteral vitamins, are usually beneficial.

If the pain is severe, opiates will be required. Morphine is the drug of choice when given in small divided doses. Cool showers have been found to be effective in relieving the severe itching. It should be kept in mind that in rare instances Scombroid poisoning may be combined with other types of fish poisoning. Fluids given to patients suffering from disturbances of temperature sensation should be either slightly warm or at room temperature. Vitamin B complex supplements are advisable.

PREVENTION:

One cannot detect a poisonous fish by its appearance. Moreover, there is no known simple chemical test to detect the poison. The most reliable methods involve either the preparation of tissue extracts which are injected intraperitoneally into mice; or feeding samples of viscera and flesh to cats or dogs, observing the animal for toxic symptoms. The viscera-liver and intestines of tropical marine fishes should never be eaten. Also, the roe of most marine fishes is potentially dangerous, and in some cases may produce rapid death. Fishes which are unusually large for their size should be eaten with caution. This is particularly true for barracuda, jacks, and groupers during their reproductive seasons. Keep in mind that an edible fish in one region may kill a person in another (27, 32, 41, 47, 48, 56, 58).

The Following Gulf of Mexico Fishes Have Been Implicated in Outbreaks of Ciguatera:

Atlantic Bonito *(Sarda sarda)*
Atlantic Moonfish, Horsefish *(Vomer setapinnis)*
Atlantic Thread Herring *(Opisthonema oglinum)*

Ballyhoo *(Hemiramphus brasiliensis)* (Fig. 235)
Banded Rudderfish *(Seriola zonata)*
Bandtail Puffer *(Sphoeroides spengleri)* (Fig. 234)
Bar Jack *(Caranx ruber)* (Fig. 219)
Big-Eye Scad *(Selar crumenophthalmus)*
Black Grouper, Jewfish, Rockfish *(Mycteroperca bonaci)* (Fig. 227)
Blue Runner *(Caranx crysos)*
Blue Shark *(Prionace glauca)*
Blunt Nose Stingray *(Dasyatis sayi)*
Bonefish *(Albula vulpes)*
Bonnethead *(Sphyrna tiburo)*
Brazilian Scorpion Fish *(Scorpaena brasiliensis)*
Common Hammerhead *(Sphyrna zygaena)*
Creole Fish *(Paranthias furcifer)* (Fig. 230)
Crevalle Jack *(Caranx hippos)* (Fig. 217)
Doctorfish *(Acanthurus chirurgus)*
Dolphin *(Coryphaena hippurus)* (Fig. 239)
Flying Gunard, Batfish *(Dactylopterus volitans)*
Gizzard Shad *(Dorosoma cepedianum)* (Fig. 233)
Gray Triggerfish *(Balistes capriscus)* (Fig. 211)
Great Barracuda *(Sphyraena barracuda)* (Fig. 176 a, b)
Greater Amberjack *(Seriola dumerili)* (Fig. 237)
Green Moray *(Gymnothorax funebris)* (Fig. 160)
Guaguanche *(Sphyraena guachancho)*
Half Beak *(Hyporhamphus unifasciatus)*
Hammerhead *(Sphyrna diplana)*
Hogfish *(Lachnolaimus maximus)* (Fig. 224)
Horse-Eye Jack *(Caranx latus)* (Fig. 218)
King Mackerel *(Scomberomorus cavalla)*
Little Tunny *(Euthynnus alletteratus)*
Lookdown *(Selene vomer)*
Mutton Snapper *(Lutjanus analis)* (Fig. 225)
Ocean Triggerfish *(Canthidermis sufflamen)* (Fig. 215)
Oceanic Skip Jack *(Euthynnus pelamis)*
Orange Filefish *(Aluterus schoepfi)* (Fig. 229)
Permit, Round Pompano *(Trachinotus falcatus)* (Fig. 236)
Planehead Filefish *(Monacanthus hispidus)*
Queen Triggerfish *(Balistes vetula)* (Fig. 238)
Rainbow Runner *(Elegatis bipinnulata)*
Red-Ear Sardine, Pilchard *(Harengula humeralis)*
Red Grouper *(Epinephelus morio)*
Red Hind *(Epinephelus guttatus)* (Fig. 222)
Remora *(Remora remora)*

Rock Hind *(Epinephelus adscensionis)* (Fig. 221)
Rough Triggerfish *(Canthidermis maculatus)*
Sargassum Fish *(Histrio histrio)* (Fig. 223)
Saucer-Eye Porgy *(Calamus calamus)* (Fig. 214)
School Master *(Lutjanus apodus)* (Fig. 226)
Scrawled Cow Fish *(Lactophrys quadricornis)* (Fig. 213)
Scrawled Filefish *(Aluterus scriptus)* (Fig. 212)
Sergeant Major *(Abudefduf saxatilus)* (Fig. 210)
Seven-Gilled Shark, Cow Shark *(Heptranchias perlo)*
Sharpnose Shark *(Rhizoprionodon terraenovae)*
Smooth Butterfly Ray *(Gymnura micrura)*
Smooth Dogfish *(Mustelus canis)*
Smooth Trunkfish *(Rhinesomus triqueter)* (Fig. 232)
Spanish Hogfish *(Bodianus rufus)* (Fig. 220)
Spotted Moray *(Gymnothorax morniga)* (Fig. 161)
Spotted Snake Eel *(Ophichthus ophis)*
Striped Mullet *(Mugil cephalus)* (Fig. 231)
Sword Fish *(Xiphias gladius)*
Vermillion Snapper *(Rhomboplites aurorubens)*
Wahoo *(Acanthocybium solandri)*
White Mullet *(Mugil curema)*
White Shark *(Carcharodon carcharias)*
Yellowfin Mojarra, Silverfish *(Gerres cinereus)*
Yellowjack *(Caranx bartholomaei)* (Fig. 216)
Yellowtail Snapper *(Ocyurus chrysurus)* (Fig. 228)

POISONOUS SCOMBROID FISHES

This heading is somewhat misleading in that all the fishes listed are, under most circumstances, edible. In this particular instance, the poisoning is due directly to inadequate preservation of the fish. This category of fishes is included, however, because of the danger that may come from eating stale scombroid fishes, particularly in tropical areas. Fishes normally contain the chemical constituent, histidine, in their flesh. When histidine is acted upon by bacteria it is apparently converted into the histamine-like substance, saurine, which can cause illness in humans that resembles a severe allergy. This histamine-like substance is produced either when scombroid fishes are left at room temperature or out in the sun for several hours. For some unknown reason, the scombroid fishes seem to be more susceptible to becoming toxic by this means than most other types of fishes.

SYMPTOMATOLOGY:

The symptoms of acute scombroid poisoning resemble those of severe allergy. Frequently, poisonous scombroid flesh can be detected immediately upon tasting it. Victims state that it has a "sharp or peppery" taste. Symptoms develop within a few minutes after eating the fish. Symptoms include intense headache, dizziness, throbbing of the large blood vessel of the neck, a feeling of dryness in the mouth, thirst, palpitation of the heart, difficulty in swallowing, nausea, vomiting, diarrhea, and abdominal pain. Within a short time the victim develops massive red welts, which are accompanied by intense itching. There is danger of shock. Deaths have been reported. Generally, acute symptoms last only 8 - 12 hours, followed by rapid recovery.

TREATMENT:

In addition to such routine procedures as evacuation of the stomach and catharsis, the use of any of the ordinary antihistaminic drugs may be found to be effective.

PREVENTION:

Under most circumstances the eating of Scombroid fishes is without danger, as long as they are properly preserved. Commercially canned fish are without the slightest danger. Scombroids should be either promptly eaten soon after capture or preserved by canning or freezing as soon as possible. Fish left in the sun for longer than 2 hours should be discarded. Examine the fish before eating, if there is any evidence of staleness, such as either pallor of the gills or an off-odor, discard the fish (4, 7, 26, 27, 30, 47, 48).

The Following Gulf of Mexico Fishes Have Been Implicated in Outbreaks of Scombrotoxicity:

Atlantic Bonito *(Sarda sarda)*
Bluefin Tuna, Horse Mackerel, Great Albacore *(Thunnus thynnus)*
Cero, Pintado, Painted Mackerel *(Scomberomorus regalis)*
Chub Mackerel *(Scomber japonicus)*
Frigate Mackerel *(Auxis thazard)*
King Mackerel *(Scomberomorus cavalla)*
Little Tunny *(Euthynnus alletteratus)*
Oceanic Bonito, Shipjack Tuna *(Euthynnus pelamis)*
Spanish Mackerel *(Scomberomorus maculatus)* (Fig. 240)
Yellowfin Tuna *(Thunnus albares)*

TETRODOTOXIC FISHES

Tetrodotoxicity is a type of fish poisoning produced by the ingestion of the puffer-like fishes (ocean sunfishes, sharp nosed puffers, the puffers proper, and the porcupine fishes). To be on the safe side, it is wise to avoid any fish that has the remarkable ability to inflate himself by gulping in large quantities of water or air. Puffers have a distinctive offensive odor, particularly when being dressed. The liver, gonads, intestines, and skin usually contain a powerful nerve poison which may produce rapid and violent death.

SYMPTOMATOLOGY:
Symptoms are typically the same as those of ciguatera, but of a greater degree. Mortality rate is more than 60% from this poisoning.

TREATMENT:
Treatment is the same as for any dangerous, life threatening poisonous ingestion; namely, gastric lavage followed with administration of a generous quantity of activated charcoal and sodium sulfate. Intravenous fluids, vigorous and continuous symptomatic therapy, and supportive care are all the attending physician can offer (2, 4, 6, 7, 22, 26, 27, 55, 56).

The Following Gulf of Mexico Fishes Have Been Implicated in Outbreaks of Tetrodotoxicity:

Bandtail Puffer *(Sphoeroides spengleri)* (Fig. 234)
Checkered Puffer *(Sphoeroides testudineus)*
Ocean Sunfish, Moonfish *(Mola mola)*
Porcupine Fish *(Diodon hystrix)* (Fig. 181 a, b)
Smooth Puffer *(Lagocephalus laevigatus)*
Striped Burrfish *(Chilomycterus schoepfi)* (Fig. 241)

PARALYTIC SHELLFISH POISONING

Ingestion of certain shellfish, the Atlantic thorny oyster *(Spondylus americanus)* in particular, can result in either infectious hepatitis or paralytic shellfish poisoning, rather than classical ciguatera (Fig. 242).

SYMPTOMS OF PARALYTIC SHELLFISH POISONING:
A variety of gastrointestinal symptoms; nausea, vomiting and parasthesia, followed later by numbness of the lips and tongue; also parasthesia and

228

numbness of the finger tips, followed by ataxia, and generalized muscular incoordination may be seen. Aphasia, attended by dryness, and a constrictive sensation in the throat have been reported. Reflexes are unaffected. Later stages may show ascending paralysis. Death may result from respiratory failure in 2 - 12 hours.

ETIOLOGY:

The poisoning is caused by a toxin produced primarily by the dinoflagellate, *Gymnodinium breve,* which is concentrated in the oyster.

TREATMENT:

Perform prompt and vigorous resuscitation. Thereafter, supportive and symptomatic therapy is indicated. Intravenous, broad spectrum antibiotics have also been of some help in the treatment of these poisonings.

MARINE LIFE

REFERENCES

1. Alender, C. B. "A Biologically Active Substance from the Spines of Two Diadematid Sea Urchins" in *Animal Toxins.* F. E. Russell and R. R. Saunders, Co-Editors, Pergamon Press Ltd., London, 1967, pp. 145-155.

2. Arena, J. *Poisoning.* 2nd ed., Charles C. Thomas, Springfield, Ill., 1970, pp. 464-472.

3. Baldridge, H. D. and J. Williams. "Shark Attack: Feeding or Fighting". *Milit. Med.* 134:130-133 (1969).

4. Banner, A. H. "Marine Toxins from the Pacific, I - Advances in the Investigation of Fish Toxins" in *Animal Toxins.* F. E. Russell and P. R. Saunders, Co-Editors, Pergamon Press Ltd., London, 1967, pp. 157-165. ·,

5. Barnes, J. H. "Extraction of Cnidarian venom from Living Tentacle" in *Animal Toxins* F. E. Russell and P. R. Saunders, Co-Editors, Pergamon Press Ltds., London, 1967, pp. 115-129.

6. Baslow, M. H. *Marine Pharmacology.* Williams and Wilkins Co., Baltimore, Md., 1969, pp. 193-244.

7. Baslow, M. H. "Marine Toxins". *Ann. Rev. Pharmacol.* 11:447-454 (1971).

8. Bitseff, E. L., W. J. Garoni, C. D. Hardison and J. M. Thompson. "The Management of Sting Ray Injuries of the Extremities". *Southern Med. J.* 63:417-418 (1970).

9. Burnett, J. W. and R. Goldner. "Effects of Chrysaora Quinquechirrha (Sea Nettle) Toxin on the Rat Cardiovascular System (34213)". *Proc. Soc. Exp. Biol. Med.* 132:353-356 (1969).

10. Burnett, J. W. and R. Goldner. "Effect of Chrysaora Quinquecirrha (Sea Nettle) Toxin on Rat Nerve and Muscle". *Toxicon* 8:179-181 (1970).

11. Burnett, J. W. and W. M. Gould. "Further Studies on the Purification and Physiological Actions of Sea Nettle Toxin". *Proc. Soc. Exp. Biol. Med.* 138:759-762 (1971).

12. Castex, M. N. "Fresh Water Venomous Rays" in *Animal Toxins.* F. E. Russell and P. R. Saunders, Co-Editors, Pergamon Press Ltd., London, 1967, pp. 167-176.

13. Clark, F. E. and C. E. Lane. "Composition of Float Gases of Physalia Physalis". *Proc. Soc. Exper. Biol. Med.* 107:673-674 (1961).

14. Clenchi, W. J. and Y. Kondo. "The Poison Cone Shell". *Amer. J. Trop. Med.* 23:105 (1943).

15. Courville, D. A., B. W. Halstead and D. W. Hessel. "Marine Biotoxins: Isolation and Properties". *Chem. Rev.* 58:235 (1958).

16. deSylva, D. P. *Studies in Tropical Oceanography No. I. Great Barracuda.* Univ. of Miami Press, Miami, 1963, pp. 121-153.

17. Endean, R., J. Izatt and D. McColm. "The Venom of the Piscivorous Gastropod Conus Striatus" in *Animal Toxins.* F. E. Russell and P. R. Saunders, Co-Editors, Pergamon Press Ltd., London, 1967, pp. 167-176.

18. Evans, M. H. "Block of Sensory Nerve Conduction in the Cat by Mussel Poison and Tetrodotoxin" in *Animal Toxins.* F. E. Russell and P. R. Saunders, Co-Editors, Pergamon Press Ltd., London, 1967, pp. 97-108.

19. Farber, L. and P. Lerke. "Studies on the Toxicity of Rhodactis howesii (Maxamalu)" in *Venomous and Poisonous Animals and Noxious Plants of the Pacific Region.* H. L. Keegan, and W. V. MacFarlane, Co-Editors, The MacMillan Co., New York, 1963, pp. 67-74.

20. Fogel, B. J. "Neurotoxicity due to Barracuda Ingestion". *J. Pediat.* 64:561-564 (1964).

21. Freeman, S. E. and R. J. Turner. "Cardiovascular Effects of Cnidarian Toxins: A Comparison of Toxins Extracted from Chiropsalmus Quadrigatus and Chironex Fleckeri". *Toxicon.* 10:31-37 (1972).

22. Ghiretti, F. and E. Rocca. "Some Experiments on Ichthyotoxin" in *Venomous and Poisonous Animals and Noxious Plants of the Pacific Region.* H. L. Keegan and W. V. MacFarlane, Co-Editors, The MacMillan Co., New York, 1963, pp. 211-216.

23. Halstead, B. W. "Venomous Coelenterates, Echinoderms, and Annelids" in *Venomous Animals and Their Venoms.* W. Bücherl and E. E. Buckley, Co-Editors, Academic Press, New York, 1971, pp. 395-440.

24. Halstead, B. W. "Venomous Echinoderms and Annelids: Starfishes, Sea Urchins, Sea Cucumbers, and Segmented Worms" in *Venomous Animals and Their Venoms.* W. Bücherl and E. E. Buckley, Co-Editors, Academic Press, New York, 1971, pp. 419-440.

25. Halstead, B. W. "Venomous Fishes" in *Venomous Animals and Their Venoms.* W. Bücherl and E. E. Buckley, Co-Editors, Academic Press, New York, 1971, pp. 588-626.

26. Halstead, B. W. *Dangerous Marine Animals.* Cornell Maritime Press, Cambridge, Md., 1959, pp. 9-136.

27. Halstead, B. W. "Fish Poisonings - their Diagnosis, Pharmacology, and Treatment". *Clin. Pharmacol. Ther.* 5:615-627 (1964).

28. Halstead, B. W. and A. E. Dalgleish. "The Venom Apparatus of the European Star-gazer Uranoscopus scaber Linnaeus" in *Animal Toxins.* F. E. Russell and P. R. Saunders, Co-Editors, Pergamon Press Ltd., London, 1967, pp. 177-186.

29. Halstead, B. W., L. B. Kuninobu and H. G. Hebard. "Catfish Stings and the Venom Apparatus of the Mexican Catfish, Galeichthys Felis (Linnaeus)". *Trans. Amer. Micr. Soc.* 72:297-313 (1953).

30. Halstead, B. W. and L. R. Mitchell. "A Review of the Venomous Fishes of the Pacific Area" in *Venomous and Poisonous Animals and Noxious Plants of the Pacific Region.* H. L. Keegan and W. V. MacFarlane, Co-Editors, The MacMillan Co., New York, 1963, pp. 173-210.

31. Hastings, S. G., J. B. Larsen and C. E. Lane. "Effects of Nematocyst Toxin of Physalia physalis (Portuguese Man-of-War) on the Canine Cardiovascular System". *Proc. Soc. Exp. Biol. Med.* 125:41 (1967).

32. Hessel, D. W. "Marine Biotoxins III. The Extraction and Partial Purification of Ciguatera Toxin from Lutjanus bohar (Forskal): Use of Silicic Acid Chromatography" in *Venomous and Poisonous Animals and Noxious Plants of the Pacific Region.* H. L. Keegan and W. V. MacFarlane, Co-Editors, The MacMillan Co., New York, 1963, pp. 203-209.

33. Ioannides, G. and J. H. Davis. "Portuguese Man-of-War Stinging". *Arch. Derm.* 91:448-451 (1965).

34. Keen, T. E. B. "Comparison of Tentacle Extracts from Chiropsalmus Quadrigatus and Chironex Fleckeri". *Toxicon.* 9:249-254 (1971).

35. Kohn, A. J. "Venomous Marine Snails of the Genus Conus" in *Venomous and Poisonous Animals and Noxious Plants of the Pacific Region.* H. L. Keegan and W. V. MacFarlane, Co-Editors, The MacMillan Co., New York, 1963, pp. 83-96.

36. Lane, C. E. "Pharmacologic Action of Physalia Toxin". *Fed. Proc.* 26:1225-1226 (1967).

37. Lane, C. E. "Recent Observations on the Pharmacology of Physalia Toxin" in *Animal Toxins.* F. E. Russell and P. R. Saunders, Co-Editors, Pergamon Press Ltd., London, 1967, pp. 131-136.

38. Lane, C. E. "The Portuguese Man-of-War". *Sci. Amer.* 202:158-163 (1960).

39. Larson, E., R. C. Lalone, E. J. de Villez and R. Siman, Jr. "Physiological and Pharmacological Studies on Extracts of the Western Atlantic Puffer Speriodes Maculatus" in *Animal Toxins.* F. E. Russell and P. R. Saunders, Co-Editors, Pergamon Press Ltd., London, 1967, pp. 187-194.

40. Marr, J. J. "Portuguese Man-of-War Envenomization". *J. A. M. A.* 199:115-116 (1967).

41. McFarren, E. F. "Differentiation of the Poisons of Fish, Shellfish and Plankton" in *Animal Toxins.* F. E. Russell and P. R. Saunders, Co-Editors, Pergamon Press Ltd., London, 1967, pp. 85-90.

42. McMichael, D. F. "Venomous Mollusks" in *Venomous Animals and Their Venoms.* W. Bücherl and E. E. Buckley, Co-Editors, Academic Press, New York, 1971 pp. 373-391.

43. McNeill, F. "Stinging Coral and So Called Stinging Seaweed". *Post Grad. Bull.* pp. 65-66 (March, 1963).

44. Middlebrook, R. E., L. E. Wittle, E. D. Scura and C. E. Lane. "Isolation and Purification of a Toxin from Millepora Dichotoma". *Toxicon.* 9:335-336 (1971).

45. Mullanney, P. J. "Treatment of Sting Ray Wounds". *Clin. Toxicol.* 3:613-615 (1970).

46. O'Neal, R. L., B. W. Halstead and L. D. Howard. "Injury to Human Tissues from Sea Urchin Spines". *Calif. Med.* 101:199-202 (1964).

47. Orris, W. L. Personal Communication.

48. Orris, W. L. "Drugs from the Sea", "Poisonous Aquatic Animals". *Acquatic Medicine* (Syllabus), Office of Continuing Education, Univ. of Calif., San Diego School of Medicine, San Diego, Calif., 1973, pp. 38-41, 63-68.

49. Parnas, I. and F. E. Russell. "Effects of Venoms on Nerve, Muscle and Neuromuscular Junction" in *Animal Toxins.* F. E. Russell and P. R. Saunders, Co-Editors, Pergamon Press Ltd., London, 1967, pp. 400-415.

50. "Poisoning by the Stingray" (Editorial). *Quart. Rev. Pediat.* 13:120-123 (1958).

51. Pope, E. C. "Some Noxious Marine Invertebrates from Australian Seas". *Post Grad. Bull.* pp. 91-102 (March, 1963).

52. Ray, S. M. and D. V. Aldrich. "Ecological Interactions of Toxic Dinoflagellates and Molluscs in the Gulf of Mexico" in *Animal Toxins.* F. E. Russell and P. R. Saunders, Co-Editors, Pergamon Press Ltd., London, 1967, pp. 75-83.

53. Russell, F. E., T. C. Panos, L. W. Kang, A. M. Warner and T. C. Colket, III. "Studies on the Mechanism of Death from Stingray Venom - A Report of Two Fatal Cases". *Amer. J. Med. Sci.* 235:566-584 (1958).

54. Russell, F. E. "Physalia Stings: A Report of Two Cases". *Toxicon.* 4:65-67 (1966).

55. Russell, F. E. "Comparative Pharmacology of Some Animal Toxins". *Fed. Proc.* 26:1206-1226 (1967).

56. Russell, F. E. "Marine Toxins and Venomous and Poisonous Marine Animals" in *Advances in Marine Biology.* F. S. Russell, Editor, Academic Press, London and New York, 1965, 3:256-369.

57. Saunders, P. R. "Venoms of Scorpionfishes". *Proc. West Pharmacol.* 2:47-54 (1959).

58. Shantz, E. J. "Studies on the Paralytic Poisonings Found in Mussels and Clams along the North American Pacific Coast" in *Venomous and Poisonous Animals and Noxious Plants of the Pacific Region.* H. L. Keegan and W. V. MacFarlane, Co-Editors, The MacMillan Co., New York, 1963, pp. 75-81.

59. Southcott, R. V. "Coelenterates and Other Marine Invertebrates 'Coelenterates of Medical Importance" in *Venomous and Poisonous Animals and Noxious Plants of the Pacific Regions.* H. L. Keegan and W. V. MacFarlane, Co-Editors, The MacMillan Co., New York, 1963, pp. 41-62.

60. Southcott, R. V. "Human Injuries from Invertebrate Animals in the Australian Seas". *Clin. Toxicol.* 3:617-636 (1970).

61. Tanous, J. G. and P. Ilano, "Predatory Fish Bites in South Florida". *Amer. Surg.* 26:443-445 (1960).

62. *U. S. Navy Diving Manual NAVSHIPS 0994-001-9010.* "Fish Bites and Stings". Navy Dept., Washington, D. C. 20350.

63. Williams, C. S. and D. C. Riordan, *"Mycobacterium marinum* (Atypical Acid-Fast Bacillus) Infections of the Hand". *J. Bone and Joint Surg.* 55-A:1042-1050 (1973).

64. Wittle, L. W., R. E. Middlebrook and C. E. Lane. "Isolation and Partial Purification of a Toxin from Millepora Alcicornis". *Toxicon.* 9:330-331(1971).

MARINE LIFE

GENERAL BIBLIOGRAPHY

1. Abbott, R. T. *A Guide to Field Identification of Seashells of North America.* Golden Press, New York, 1968, pp. 160-163.

2. Andrews, J. *Sea Shells of Texas Coast.* Univ. Texas Press, Austin and London, 1971.

3. Arnold, A. F. *The Sea-Beach at Ebb-Tide.* Dover Publications, Inc., New York, 1968.

4. Bailey, R. M. "List of the Common and Scientific Names of Fishes from the U. S. and Canada". 3rd Ed., *Amer. Fish. Soc.,* Spec. Publ. 6, Washington, D. C. (1970).

5. Barnes, R. D. *Invertebrate Zoology.* W. B. Saunders Co., Philadelphia, 1968.

6. Barrington, E. J. W. *Invertebrate Structure and Function.* Houghton Mifflin Co., Boston, 1967.

7. Baughman, J. L. and S. Springer. "Biological and Economic Notes on the Sharks of the Gulf of Mexico, with Special Reference to those of Texas and with a Key for Their Identification". *Amer. Midland Naturalist.* 44:96-152 (1950).

8. Bayer, F. M. and H. B. Owre. *The Free-Living Lower Invertebrates.* The MacMillan Co., New York, 1968.

9. Blackwelder, R. E. *Guide to the Taxonomic Literature of Vertebrates.* Iowa State Univ. Press, Ames, Iowa, 1972.

10. Boolootian, R. A., Ed. *Physiology of Echinodermata.* Interscience Publishers, New York, 1966.

11. Breder, C. M., Jr. *Field Book of Marine Fishes of the Atlantic Coast.* 11th ed., G. P. Putnam's Sons, New York and London, 1948.

12. Bright, T. and L. Pequegnat, Ed. *Biota of the West Flower Garden Bank.* Gulf Publishing Co., Houston, 1973.

13. Buchsbaum, R. and L. J. Milne. *Lower Animals.* Doubleday and Co., New York, 1972.

14. Buckley, E. E. and N. Porges. *Venoms.* American Association for the Advancement of Science, Washington, 44:9-27 (1956).

15. Budker, P. *The Life of Sharks.* Columbia Univ. Press, New York, 1971.

16. Cook, J. J. and W. L. Wisner. *Nightmare World of the Shark.* Dodd, Mead, and Co., New York, 1968.

17. Davies, D. H. and G. D. Campbell. "The Aetiology, Clinical Pathology and Treatment of Shark Attack". *J. R. Nav. Med. Serv.* 48:110-136 (1962).

18. De Sylva, D. P. *Systematics and Life History of the Great Barracuda (Sphyraena barracuda).* Univ. Miami Press, 1963.

19. Eddy, S. *How to Know the Freshwater Fishes.* W. C. Brown Co., Iowa, 1957.

20. Gallaway, J. B., J. C. Parker and D. Moore. *Key to the Estuarine and Marine Fishes of Texas.* 2nd ed. J. C. Parker, Ed., Texas A&M Univ., 1972.

21. Galstoff, P. S. "The Gulf of Mexico, Its Origin, Waters, and Marine Life". *Fishery Bull. of Fisheries and Wildlife Serv.* Washington, D. C. 55, Bull. 59, p. 92 (1954).

22. Gilbert, P. W., Ed. *Sharks and Survival.* D. C. Heath Co., Boston, 1963.

23. Gill, T. "Life Histories of Toad Fishes Compared with Those of Weevers and Stargazers". *Smithsonian Insti. Publ.,* Misc. Coll., 48:391-422 (1967).

24. Gosner, K. L. *Guide to the Identification of Marine and Estuarine Invertebrates.* Wiley-Interscience, New York, 1971.

25. Grant, L. J., Ed. "Wondrous World of Fishes". *National Geographic Society,* Washington, D. C., 1969.

26. Greenwood, P. H., D. E. Rosen, S. H. Weitzman and G. S. Myers "Phyletic Studies of Teleostean Fishes with Provisional Classification of Living Forms". *Bull. Amer. Mus. Nat. Hist.* 131:341-455 (1966).

27. Halstead, B. W. *Dangerous Marine Animals.* Cornell Maritime Press, Cambridge, Md., 1959.

28. Halstead, B. W. *Poisonous and Venomous Marine Animals of the World.* U. S. Govt. Printing Office, Washington, D. C., 3 vols., 1965.

29. Herald, E. S. *Living Fishes of the World.* Doubleday, Garden City, New York, 1961.

30. Jordan, D. S. and B. W. Evermann. *Fishes of North and Middle America.* U. S. Govt. Printing Office, Washington, D. C., 4 vols., 1963.

31. Lagler, K. R., J. E. Bardach and R. R. Miller. *Ichthyology.* John Wiley and Sons, Inc., New York, 1963.

32. Lane, F. W. *Kingdom of the Octopus. The Life History of Cephalopoda.* Sheridan House, New York, 1960.

33. Marshall, N. B. *Exploration in the Life of Fishes.* Harvard Univ. Press, Cambridge, Mass., 1971.

34. Marshall, N. B. *Life of Fishes.* World Press, Cleveland, 1966.

35. Milne, L. J. and M. J. G. Milne. *Invertebrates of North America.* Doubleday and Co., New York, 1972.

36. Newell, R. C. *Biology of Intertidal Animals.* Elsevier Publishing Co., Inc., New York, 1970.

37. Nichols, D. and J. A. Cooke. *Oxford Book of Invertebrates.* Oxford Univ. Press, London, 1971.

38. Phillips, C. and W. H. Brady. *Sea Pests, Poisonous or Harmful Sea Life of Florida and West Indies.* Publ. of Marine Lab., Univ. Miami Press, 1953.

39. Randall, J. E. *Caribbean Reef Fishes.* T. F. H. Publications, Inc., Jersey City, N. J., 1968.

40. Reed, C. T. *Marine Life in Texas Waters.* Texas Academy Publ. Nat. Hist. Anson Jones Press, Houston, 1941.

41. Ricketts, E. F. and J. Calvin. *Between Pacific Tides.* Stanford Univ. Press, Stanford, Calif., 1968.

42. Roche, E. T. and B. W. Halstead. "Venom Apparatus of California Rockfishes (Family Scorpaenidae)". *Calif. Depart. Fish and Game,* Long Beach, Calif., Fish Bull. 156:4-49 (1972).

43. Russell-Hunter, W. D. *A Biology of Higher Invertebrates.* The MacMillan Co., London, 1971.

44. Russell-Hunter, W. D. *A Biology of Lower Invertebrates.* The MacMillan Co., London, 1971.

45. Rudloe, J. *The Erotic Ocean.* World Publishing, New York, 1971.

46. Springer, S. "Natural History of the Lemon Shark". *Texas J. Sci.* 3:349-359 (1950).

47. Stocik, R. D. *The Sharks Around Us.* Star Publishing Co., Boynton Beach, Florida, 1971.

48. Thorson, G. *Life in the Sea.* McGraw-Hill Book Co., New York, 1971.

49. Walton-Smith, F. G. *Atlantic Reef Corals.* Univ. Miami Press, Coral Gables, Florida, 1971.

50. Wood, E. J. F. *Dinoflagellates of the Caribbean and Adjacent Areas.* Univ. Miami Press, Coral Gables, Florida, 1968.

Fig. 150. PURPLE SEA URCHIN
(Arbacia punctulata)

(Photo by A. Campos)

(Photo by S. H. Reuter)

Fig. 151. BLACK SEA URCHIN
(Diadema antillarum)

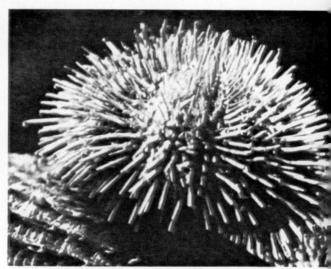

(From Halstead, <u>Poisonous</u> <u>and</u> <u>Venomous</u> <u>Marine</u> <u>Animals</u>, Vol. 1)

Fig. 152. WHITE SEA URCHIN
(Lytechinus variegatus)

Fig. 153. SEA EGG
(Tripneustes ventricosus)

(Photo by R. Zingula)

Fig. 154 a. POLYCHAETE WORM
(Eunice sp.)

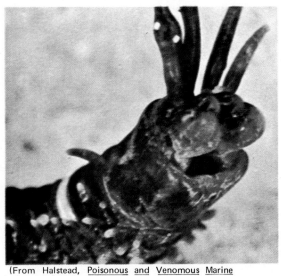

Fig. 154 b. POLYCHAETE WORM MOUTH.

Fig. 155 a. MANTIS SHRIMP
(Gonodactylus bredini)

Fig. 155 b. MANTIS SHRIMP FEELERS &
POSTERIOR SPINES.

Fig. 156. BRIEF SQUID
(Lolliguncula brevis)

Fig. 157. COMMON OCTOPUS
(Octopus vulgaris)

(Photo by E. Alexander)

Fig. 158. OCTOPUS "BEAK"

(Photo by S. H. Reuter)
Fig. 159. KNIFE IN OCTOPUS MOUTH.

Fig. 160. GREEN MORAY *(Gymnothorax funebris)*

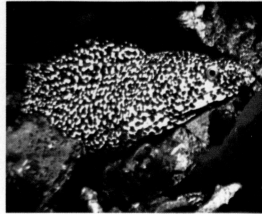

(Photo by S. H. Reuter)
Fig. 161. COMMON SPOTTED MORAY
EEL *(Gymnothorax moringa)*

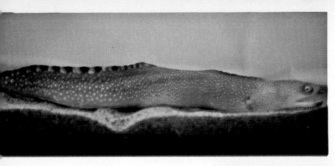

Fig. 162. BLACK-EDGE
MORAY EEL
(Gymnothorax nigromarginatus)

Fig. 163. GREEN TURTLE
(Chelonia mydas)

(Photo by S. H. Reuter)

Fig. 164. LEATHERBACK TURTLE
(Dermochelys coriacea)

(From Halstead, Poisonous and Venomous Marine Animals, Vol. 3)

(From Halstead, Poisonous and Venomous Marine Animals, Vol. 3)

Fig. 165. HAWKSBILL TURTLE
(Eretmochelys imbricata)

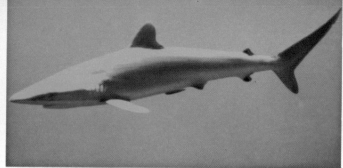

(Photo by T. L. Turnbull)

Fig. 166. SILKY SHARK *(Carcharhinus falciformes)*

Fig. 167. BULL SHARK *(Carcharhinus leucas)*

(Photo by A. Campos)

Fig. 168. BLACKTIP SHARK *(Carcharhinus limbatus)*

Fig. 169. NURSE SHARK *(Ginglymostoma cirratum)*

(Photo by E. Alexander)

Fig. 170. OCEANIC WHITETIP SHARK *(Carcharhinus longimanus)*

(Photo by T. L. Turnbull)

Fig. 171. LEMON SHARK *(Negaprion brevirostris)*

Fig. 172. SCALLOPED HAMMERHEAD *(Sphyrna lewini)*

(Photo by A. Campos)

Fig. 173. DOGFISH SHARK *(Squalus acanthias)*

Fig. 174. SURVIVOR OF SHARK ATTACK.

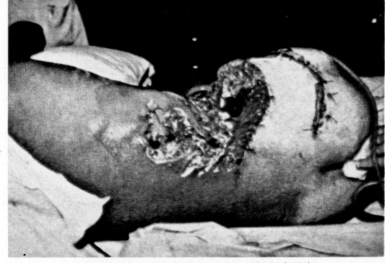

(From Davies & Campbell, J. Royal Naval Medical Service, 48:110 (1962)

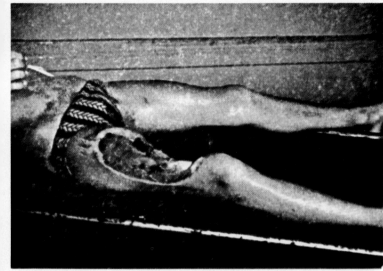

Fig. 175. SHARK
ATTACK ENDING IN
FATALITY.

(From Davies & Campbell, J. Royal Naval Medical Service, 48:110 (1962)

Fig. 176 a. GREAT
BARRACUDA *(Sphyraena
barracuda)*

Fig. 176 b. GREAT
BARRACUDA *(Sphyraena
barracuda)*

(Photo by S. H. Reuter)

(Photo by H. Vance)
Fig. 177. SOUTHERN STARGAZER
(Astroscopus y-graecum)

(Photo by J. Coffield)
Fig. 180. ALLIGATOR
GAR
(Lepisosteus spatula)

Fig. 178. GAFF-TOP SAIL CATFISH *(Bagre marinus)*

Fig. 179. SEA CATFISH
(Arius felis)

(Photo by S. H. Reuter)

Fig. 181 a. PORCUPINE FISH *(Diodon hystrix)* (Deflated)

(Photo by S. H. Reuter)

Fig. 181 b. PORCUPINE FISH *(Diodon hystrix)* (Inflated)

(Photo by S. H. Reuter)

Fig. 182. SQUIRREL FISH
(Holocentrus ascensionis)

Fig. 183. GULF TOADFISH *(Opsanus beta)*

(From Halstead, Poisonous & Venomous Marine Animals, Vol. 3)

Fig. 184. SPOTTED EAGLE RAY
(Aetobatus narinari)

Fig. 185. SOUTHERN STINGRAY
(Dasyatis americana)

Fig. 186. STINGAREE
(Dasyatis sabina)

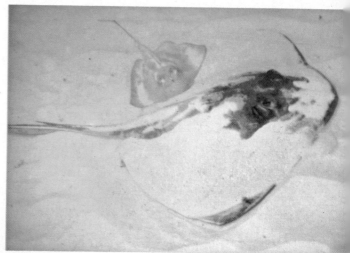

(Photo by S. H. Reuter

Fig. 187. LESSER ELECTRIC RAY
(Narcine brasiliensis)

Fig. 188. YELLOW
SPOTTED STINGRAY
(Urolophus jamaicensis)

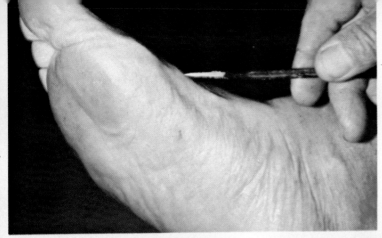

Fig. 189. STINGRAY BARB & TYPICAL PUNCTURE WOUND.

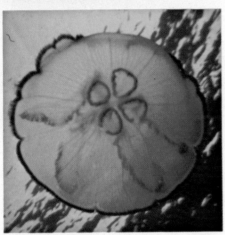

(Photo by S. H. Reuter)

Fig. 190. MOON JELLY
(Aurelia aurita)

(Photo by E. Alexander)

Fig. 191. ELKHORN CORAL *(Acropora palmata)*

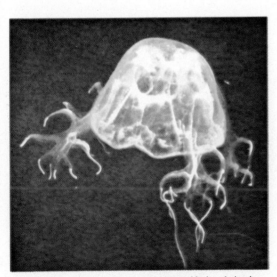

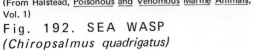

(From Halstead, Poisonous and Venomous Marine Animals, Vol. 1)

Fig. 192. SEA WASP
(Chiropsalmus quadrigatus)

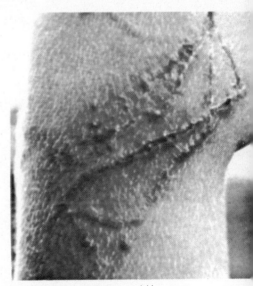

(From Halstead, Poisonous and Venomous Marine Animals, Vol. 1)

Fig. 193. SEA WASP WOUND ON KNEE ONE WEEK AFTER STINGING.

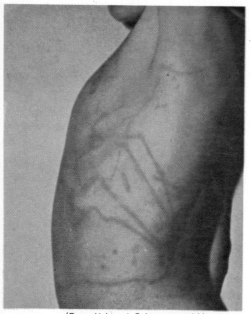

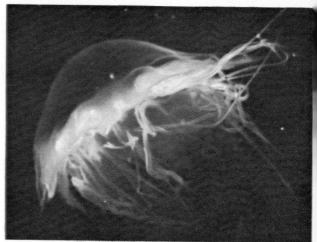

(Photo by T. L. Turnbull)
Fig. 194. HAIRY STINGER, LION'S MANE
(Cyanea capillata)

(From Halstead, <u>Poisonous</u> <u>and</u> <u>Venomous</u>
<u>Marine</u> <u>Animals</u>, Vol. 1)
Fig. 195. HAIRY STINGER WOUND
ONE HOUR AFTER STING.

(Photo by S. H. Reuter)

Fig. 196 a. FIRE CORAL
(Millipora complanta)

(Photo by D. Bowman)

Fig. 196 b. FIRE CORAL
WITH FEATHERDUSTER
WORM *(Millipora complanta)*

Fig. 196 c. FIRE CORAL
(Millipora complanta)

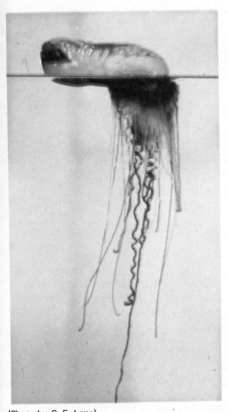

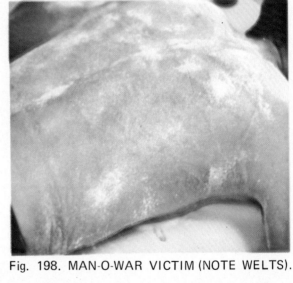

Fig. 198. MAN-O-WAR VICTIM (NOTE WELTS).

Fig. 197. PORTUGUESE
MAN-O-WAR *(Physalia physalis)*

Fig. 199. MAN-O-WAR TREATMENT
INCLUDES ALCOHOL & ADOLPH'S
MEAT TENDERIZER.

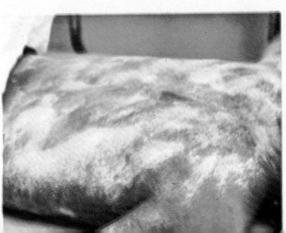

Fig. 200. BRISTLE WORM,
SEA MOUSE *(Chloeia viridis)*

(From Halstead, <u>Poisonous</u> <u>and</u> <u>Venomous</u> <u>Marine</u> <u>Animals</u>, Vol. 1)

Fig. 201. FIRE WORM
(Eurythroe complanta)

(From Halstead, <u>Poisonous</u> <u>and</u> <u>Venomous</u> <u>Marine</u> <u>Animals</u>, Vol. 1)

Fig. 202. BRISTLE WORM
(Hermodice carunculata)

(Photo by S. H. Reuter)

Fig. 203. SEA CUCUMBER
(Stichopus bandiotus)

(From Halstead, <u>Poisonous</u> <u>and</u> <u>Venomous</u> <u>Marine</u> <u>Animals</u>, Vol. 1)

(Photo by A. Campos)
Fig. 204. ALPHABET CONE *(Conus spurius)*

Fig. 205. FLORIDA CONE
(Conus floridanus)

Fig. 206. ATLANTIC AGATE
CONE *(Conus ranunculus)*

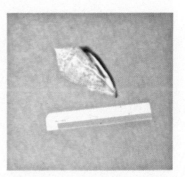

Fig. 207. SOZON'S CONE
(Conus sozoni)

Fig. 208 a. WEST INDIAN SCORPION FISH *(Scorpaena plumieri)*

(From Halstead, <u>Poisonous</u> <u>and</u> <u>Venomous</u> <u>Marine</u> <u>Animals</u>, Vol. 3)

Fig. 208 b. WEST INDIAN SCORPION FISH - WELL CAMOUFLAGED.

(Photo by T. L. Turnbull)

MARINE HABITATS

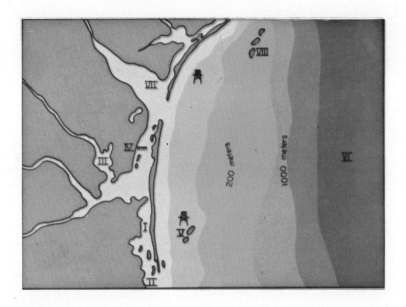

Fig. 209

    I.   Protected outer coast: rocky coast, sandy beaches, tidal pools.

    II.   Open coast: rocky shores, sandy beaches, surf zone.

    III. Bays and estuaries: rocky shores, sand flats, eel-grass communities, mud flats.

   IV. Wharf pilings: exposed pilings, protected pilings.

    V.   Offshore barrier reefs and shallow waters a short distance away from the coast: oil rigs, tropical lagoons.

   VI. Open Seas.

  VII. Inland brackish waters and rivers: river deltas.

 VIII. Reefs of deep water.

The Roman numerals indicated on the above map correspond to the various habitat areas of the Gulf of Mexico. These same numerals are utilized in the following sections on Ciguatoxic, Scombrotoxic, Tetrodotoxic, and Shellfish Poisoning to indicate the normal habitat in which the various seasonally poisonous fishes are found.

CIGUATOXIC FISHES

(Photo by S. H. Reuter)

Fig. 210. SERGEANT MAJOR; DAMSEL FISH *(Abudefdux saxatilis)*
HAB: I, V   SZ: 6 in.

Fig. 211. GRAY TRIGGERFISH; LEATHER JACKET *(Balistes capriscus)*
HAB: II   SZ: 1 ft.

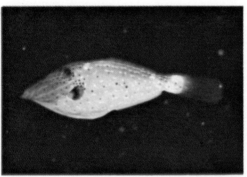

(Photo by S. H. Reuter)

Fig. 212. SCRAWLED FILEFISH; UNICORN FISH *(Aluterus scriptus)*
HAB: VI   SZ: 2-3 ft.

(Photo by S. H. Reuter)

Fig. 213. SCRAWLED COWFISH *(Lactrophrys quadricornis)*
HAB: V   SZ: 1 ft.

(Photo by T. L. Turnbull)

Fig. 214. SAUCER-EYE PORGY *(Calamus calamus)*
HAB: V   SZ: 15 in.

(Photo by A. Campos)

Fig. 215. OCEAN TRIGGERFISH; SOBACO *(Canthidermis sufflamen)*
HAB: II, V   SZ: 1 ft.

(From Randall, Caribbean Reef Fishes)

Fig. 216. YELLOWJACK; CIBI AMARILLO
(Caranx bartholomaei)
HAB: VI   SZ: 15 in.

(Photo by S. H. Reuter)

Fig. 217. CREVALLE JACK;
HORSE CREVALLE *(Caranx hippos)*
HAB: VI   SZ: 2½ ft.   WT: 20 lb.

(From Randall, Caribbean Reef Fishes)

Fig. 218. HORSE-EYE JACK *(Caranx latus)*
HAB: VI   SZ: 2 ft.

(From Randall, Caribbean Reef Fishes)

Fig. 219. BAR JACK; CARBONERO; SKIP
JACK *(Caranx ruber)*
HAB: VI   SZ: 1 ft.

(From Randall, Caribbean Reef Fishes)

Fig. 220. SPANISH HOGFISH *(Bodianus
rufus)*
HAB: VII   SZ: 8-24 in.

(Photo by S. H. Reuter)

Fig. 221. ROCK HIND; CABRAMORA;
GARRUPA *(Epinephelus adscensionis)*
HAB: V   SZ: 18 in.   WT: 8 lb.

(Photo by S. H. Reuter)

Fig. 222. RED HIND *(Epinephelus guttatus)*
HAB: VI   SZ: 1½ ft.

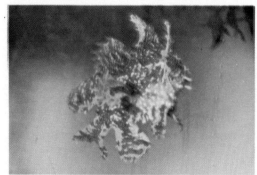

(Photo by A. Campos)

Fig. 223. SARGASSUMFISH *(Histrio histrio)*
HAB: II   SZ: 2-6 in.

(From Randall, Caribbean Reef Fishes)

Fig. 224. HOGFISH; CAPITAINE
(Lachnolaimus maximus)
HAB: V   SZ: 3 ft.   WT: 12-15 lb.

(From Randall, Caribbean Reef Fishes)

Fig. 225. MUTTON SNAPPER; PARGO
(Lutjanus analis)
HAB: VI   SZ: 27 in.   WT: 25 lb.

(From Randall, Caribbean Reef Fishes)

Fig. 226. SCHOOL MASTER *(Lutjanus
apodus)*
HAB: VI   SZ:9-18 in.   WT: 2-8 lb.

(Photo by S. H. Reuter)

Fig. 227. BLACK GROUPER; JEWFISH;
ROCKFISH *(Mycteroperca bonaci)*
HAB: Juveniles II   SZ: 4 ft.   WT: 100 lb.
        Adults VI

(Photo by J. Merritt)

Fig. 228. YELLOWTAIL SNAPPER *(Ocyurus chrysurus)*
HAB: VI, II   SZ: 2 ft.   WT: 1-6 lb.

Fig. 229. ORANGE FILEFISH *(Aluterus schoepfi)*
HAB: III   SZ: 20 in.

(Photo by E. Alexander)

Fig. 230. CREOLE FISH *(Paranthias furcifer)*
HAB: I   SZ: 1 ft.

Fig. 231. STRIPED MULLET; COMMON MULLET *(Mugil cephalus)*
HAB: VI, VIII   SZ: 15 in.

(Photo by S. H. Reuter)

Fig. 232. SMOOTH TRUNKFISH *(Rhinesomus triqueter)*
HAB: V   SZ: 10 in.

Fig. 233. GIZZARD SHAD *(Dorosoma cepedianum)*
HAB: II, III   SZ: 15 in.

Fig. 234. BANDTAIL PUFFER *(Sphoeroides spengleri)*
HAB: V   SZ: 1 ft.

Fig. 235. BALLYHOO *(Hemiramphus brasiliensis)*
HAB: II   SZ: 15 in.

(From Halstead, <u>Poisonous</u> <u>and</u> <u>Venomous</u> <u>Marine</u> <u>Animals</u>, Vol. 2)
Fig. 236. PERMIT; ROUND POMPANO *(Trachinotus falcatus)*
HAB: VI   SZ: 3½ ft.   WT: 50 lb.

(From Halstead, <u>Poisonous</u> <u>and</u> <u>Venomous</u> <u>Marine</u> <u>Animals</u>, Vol. 2)
Fig. 237. GREATER AMBERJACK *(Seriola dumerili)*
HAB: VI   SZ: 6 ft.   WT: 149 lb.

(Photo by E. Alexander)
Fig. 238. QUEEN TRIGGERFISH; OLD WIFE *(Balistes vetula)*
HAB: V   SZ: 1½ ft.

(Photo by A. Campos)
Fig. 239. DOLPHIN *(Coryphaena hippurus)*
HAB: VI   SZ: 6 ft.
WT: 85 lb.

SCOMBROTOXIC FISH

Fig. 240. SPANISH MACKEREL
(Scomberomorus maculatus)
HAB: V, VI   SZ: 4 ft.   WT: 25 lb.

TETRODOTOXIC FISH

Fig. 241. STRIPED BURRFISH
(Chilomycterus schoepfi)
HAB: II   SZ: 6-10 in.

SHELLFISH POISONING

(Photo by A. Campos)

Fig. 242. ATLANTIC THORNY
OYSTER *(Spondylus americanus)*
HAB: V   SZ: 3-4 in.

INDEX

INDEX

Bladderpod, 60
Blue fin tuna, 227
Blue runner, 225
Blue shark, 225
Blunt nose stingray, 225
Bodianus rufus, 226
Bombus spp., 174
Bonefish, 225
Bonito,
      Atlantic, 224, 227
      Oceanic, 227
Bonnethead shark, 225
Brazilian scorpion fish, 225
Brazil rattlebox, 60
Brief squid, 196
Bristle worms,
      Bristle worm, 215
      Fire worm, 215
      Sea mouse, 215
Broadbanded copperhead, 92
Brown recluse spider, 171-172
Brown spider, 171
Buckeye, red, 47
Buckeye, Texas, 47
Bull shark, 200, 201
Bumble bee, 174
Bunchberry, 13
Burrfish, striped, 228
Burring phenomenon, 133, 135, 138, 139
Buttercup, 70
Butterfly ray, smooth, 226

Caesalpinia gilliesii, 29
Caladium spp., 9
Caladium, 9
Calamus calamus, 226
Calcium oxalate, 10, 42, 48, 53
Camas, death, 71
Canebrake rattlesnake, 127
Canthidermis maculatus, 225
Canthidermis sufflamen, 225
Caranx bartholomaei, 226
Caranx crysos, 225
Caranx hippos, 225
Caranx latus, 225
Caranx ruber, 225
Carcharhinus falciformes, 200, 201

Carcharinus leucas, 200, 201
Carcharhinus limbatus, 200, 201
Carcharhinus longimanus, 200, 201
Carcharodon carcharias, 226
Cardinal flower, 66
Cardioactive glycosides, 18, 26, 33, 40
Carolina cherrylaurel, 35
Carolina horsenettle, 58
Carolina jessamine, 74
Carrot, wild, 50
Castor bean, 11
Castor oil plant, 11
Caterpillar, puss, 172
Catfish,
      Common sea, 206
      Gaff-top sail, 205
      Hard head sea, 206
Cat shark, 200
Centruroides vittatus, 173
Centruroides sculpturatus, 174
Ceriman, 9
Cero, 227
Cestrum diurnum, 14
Cestrum nocturnum, 14
Checkered puffer, 228
Chelonia mydas, 199
Cherry,
      Cultivated, 35
      Jerusalem, 40
      Natal, 40
      Wild, 51
      Wild black, 35
Cherrylaurel, 35
Chilomycterus schoepfi, 228
China tree, 31
Chinese tallow tree, 39
Chinaberry tree, 31
Chiropsalmus quadrigatus, 212
Chloeia viridis, 215
Chokecherry, 35, 36
Christmas holly, 29
Christmas mistletoe, 57
Chub mackerel, 227
Cicuta maculata, 50
Cicutoxin, 51
Ciguatera, 190, 223, 224
Ciguatoxic fishes, 198, 200, 203, 209, 223-226

269

White shark, 162, 226
Whitetip shark, oceanic, 200, 201
Wild,
    Carrot, 50
    Cherry, 51
    Cherry, black, 36
    Onion, 71
    Plum, 35
Wild balsam-apple, 55
Wild black cherry, 35, 36
Wisteria, 29, 30
Wisteria spp. 29, 30
Wyeth coral snake antivenin, 139
Wyeth Polyvalent Crotalidae antivenin, 136,
    137, 139

Xiphias gladius, 226

Yaupon, 29
Yaupon holly, 29
Yellowfin mojarra, 226
Yellowfin tuna, 227
Yellowjack, 226
Yellow jacket, 174
Yellow jessamine, 74
Yellow spotted stingray, 210, 211
Yellowtail snapper, 226
Yew, Japanese, 34
Yew, Southern, 34
Youpon, 29

Zygadenus nuttallii, 71